Wild Orchids of Sussex

David Lang

The publication of this book has been made possible by major sponsorship from English Nature, with further significant support from East Sussex County Council.

The publishers and the author also wish to thank three individuals who generously underwrote the costs of the project in its precarious early stages: Alan Perry, Paul Harmes and John Patmore, the latter 'privileged to support this book as a naturalist who loves Sussex and botany in equal measure.'

Published by Pomegranate Press, Dolphin House, 51 St Nicholas Lane, Lewes, Sussex BN7 2JZ

Front cover: Green-winged orchids at Peacehaven
Back cover: Burnt Orchids, late-flowering form, at Litlington

By the same author:
Orchids of Britain (OUP, 1980)
A Guide to the Wild Orchids of Great Britain and Ireland (OUP 1989)
The Complete Book of British Berries (Threshold Books 1987)

Other natural history titles published by Pomegranate Press:
The Sussex Tree Book (Owen Johnson)
Living Sussex (David Arscott)

ISBN: 0-9533493-3-0

British Library Cataloguing-in-Publication Data.
A catalogue record for this book is available from the British Library

Colour origination and printing by Viscan Graphics, 40 Mimosa Road, Singapore 808002

Contents

Acknowledgements

It really isn't my fault! It all started at a lecture – on a subject unrelated to orchids – during question time. 'Why isn't there a book on Sussex orchids? There's one for Dorset, Hampshire and the Isle of Wight: why not Sussex?' The question had a partisan ring to it. 'You should do it!' Ah!

I canvassed opinion among botanical friends and, to my surprise, they were entirely in agreement. What has been even more encouraging is that their enthusiasm and helpfulness have not faltered in the ensuing year. Data, records and anecdote have flowed in a generous stream from botanists in Sussex and beyond. To all those helpers I offer my grateful thanks and hope that they will feel that this book is truly theirs as well as mine.

It is a great pleasure to offer my thanks to all those in the museum and archive services, who have been, without exception, immensely helpful and have sought out so much extra material of whose existence I was ignorant. I have met with universal kindness and enthusiasm. In particular I should like to thank:

Julian Porter of Bexhill Museum
Ian Bevis of the Civic Museum, Tunbridge Wells
Dr Gerald Legg of the Booth Museum of Natural History, Brighton
Dr Roy Vickery of the British Museum of Natural History
Dr Phillip Cribb and Dr T. Cope of the Orchid Herbarium, Kew
Dr S.L. Jury of the Reading University Herbarium
Henri Brocklebank and colleagues of the Biodiversity Records Centre, Sussex Wildlife Trust
Joan Lennon and colleagues of English Nature, Lewes
Dr Rosalind Hardiman of Portsmouth City Council Museum
Dr Tim Rich and Dr George Hutchinson of the National Museum of Wales

I acknowledge with pleasure the help I have received from members of the Sussex Botanical Recording Society, in particular Mary Briggs OBE, Paul Harmes and Arthur Hoare. My thanks also to Dr David Streeter of the University of Sussex for all his help and advice.

One of the most stressful things I had to do was become computerised. I must confess deep-rooted Luddite tendencies where these machines are concerned, and without the help of Simon Linington, Kate Ryland and Max Aitken I should have been in dire trouble.

I am deeply grateful to my friends and scrutineers Dr Francis Rose MBE, Dr Nick Sturt and Alan Knapp, who have most kindly read and criticised the draft text.

To Pat Donovan, who has provided all the line drawings for the book, my grateful thanks.

Introduction

Born and bred in Kent, I have been fortunate to have spent the last thirty-five years of my professional life as a veterinary surgeon in Sussex, where I have been able to pursue an interest in our native orchids. Sussex can boast a total of thirty-three species, plus three other 'possibles', making it one of the best 'orchid counties' in the British Isles.

It all started at school, where I discovered an old book in the biology laboratory library which contained beautiful watercolour illustrations of British orchids. I found them fascinating for their colours and bizarre shapes, and secretly vowed that one day I would find them all in Britain, a vow which took me more than thirty years to fulfil and involved travelling to every corner of the British Isles.

My 'first' find was common enough – Early-purple Orchid in a damp wood just outside Tonbridge in Kent. I can still remember the thrill of seeing the Lady's-slipper (*Cypripedium calceolus*) in Yorkshire, long before it was fenced in and guarded by wardens – a sadly necessary precaution - and finding, while feverishly swatting at a cloud of vicious horse-flies, the tiny green Bog Orchid (*Hammarbya paludosa*) in a New Forest bog . Then there have been the rare occasions when I have found orchids by the the thousand where I had expected just a handful, orchids colouring the Sussex downland grass in a pink or mauve haze as far as the eye could see. Magic moments indeed!

Orchid Habitats in Sussex gives a brief summary of the geology and geography of our county, as it affects the orchids we can expect to find. **Records and Rumours** explains the reasons for recording – and the pitfalls that can result.

On the downs near the coast at High and Over, with a stunning display of the Pyramidal Orchid, ***Anacamptis pyramidalis.***

Sussex Botanologia contains short biographies of the botanists who had a particular love of the orchids of Sussex, including some very colourful 'characters', and covers the period from the mid-17th century to the present day. There follow chapters on **The Structure of Orchid Flowers** and the manner in which they develop and reproduce.

In the chapter on **Classification** I have arranged the species in the order used in my *Guide to the Wild Orchids of Great Britain and Ireland*, and kept to the same nomenclature. Current studies on the DNA phylogeny of plants may lead to changes in some of the scientific names, particularly those of the Marsh and Spotted Orchids (*Dactylorhiza*), but for the moment it was felt better to stick to the familiar names.

Mapping sets out the manner in which plants are recorded, and how to trace localities from the reference numbers used. The description of each species is accompanied by a map showing both the present and previous distribution of the species in Sussex.

Sussex has a wide variety of landscapes. A mature beech wood like this one at Dallington favours Bird's-nest Orchid and the helleborines.

Distribution maps are always a source of contention. Even if a plant was recorded in a site last year, there is no 100 per cent certainty that it still exists, and it is simply not possible to check every site for every species. Where sites have been destroyed, or the plants absent for a reasonable length of time, this is indicated, but the maps must remain essentially an optimistic record.

In **The Species** there is a full description of each orchid, with full colour illustrations and a distribution map. I have endeavoured to find as much information as possible on the past history of each orchid species in Sussex. For this I have drawn on such published material as Arnold's *Flora of Sussex* (1887), Wolley-Dod's *Flora of Sussex* (1937), Hall's *Sussex Plant Atlas* (1980 and supplements) and the recent *Flora of Ashdown Forest* (1996). I have also visited museums and herbaria throughout Sussex and beyond, and drawn upon numerous personal communications from fellow botanists.

The Factoid File describes three orchids for which there is no proof that they have really occurred in Sussex, with two species that have been introduced. Following this are **Some Notes on Hybrid Orchids in Sussex**, which I hope will help readers identify some of this most awkward group.

I have listed all the **Herbaria** which I have visited during the preparation of this book, following which there is a full **Bibliography**, a **Glossary** of the scientific terms used in the text, and an **Index**.

Inevitably there will be sites in Sussex of which I am ignorant. I welcome any information which will increase our knowledge of the county's orchids, and data on rare or threatened species will be kept confidential.

Orchid Habitats in Sussex

Anyone interested in the vegetation of the county and the manner in which it influences the flora, can do no better than read The Habitats and Vegetation of Sussex written by Dr Francis Rose (1995), and published by the Booth Museum of Natural History, Brighton. I am indebted to Dr Rose for his permission to use his material in preparing this section, and to follow his scheme of description.

West Sussex Coastal Plain

A study of the map of Sussex shows the coastal plain stretching from Chichester Harbour in the west to Brighton in the east, where the chalk downs hedge it into the sea. So much of the area is covered in housing that little remains of suitable orchid habitat. Indeed, as one old Sussex character remarked on looking at a then-recent development: 'When I looks at it, it makes me fair prostrate with dismal'.

A few pockets of wetmarsh still survive, in which there are small colonies of Marsh Orchids, both Early Marsh Orchid (*Dactylorhiza incarnata*) and Common Marsh Orchid (*Dactylorhiza praetermissa*), and in addition one huge colony of Green-winged Orchid (*Orchis morio*) with a population in excess of 60,000 flowering plants, and one good colony of Marsh Fragrant Orchid (*Gymnadenia conopsea* ssp. *densiflora*) near Chichester. Other small relict populations cling on on the edges of waterways, on golf courses and in churchyards.

The South Downs – Dip Slope

This rises gradually from the coastal plain in West Sussex, and for the most part is under cultivation. West of the river Arun there is extensive woodland, some of which may even be primary woodland which has historically never been cleared. These woods are quite unlike the scattered woodlands of East Sussex, many of which are of recent planting. The older hold healthy populations of all the more common woodland orchids, such as the Bird's-nest Orchid (*Neottia nidus-avis*) and the Fly Orchid (*Ophrys insectifera*), but there are also woods in which the rare Sword-leaved Helleborine (*Cephalanthera longifolia*) still occurs, and where the even rarer Red Helleborine (*C.rubra*) has been reported.

The south-facing downland slopes are limited in extent, but at reserves such as Harting Downs and Levin Down, and the slopes above Kingley Vale, there are good populations of Frog Orchid (*Coeloglossum viride*), Autumn Lady's-tresses (*Spiranthes spiralis*) and Pyramidal Orchid (*Anacamptis pyramidalis*).

The best south-facing chalk grassland lies east of Brighton, where the National Nature Reserve at Castle Hill hosts seven orchid species, with a particularly fine population of Early Spider-orchid (*Ophrys sphegodes*). Further to the east the slopes of The Caburn and the valley sides of the Cuckmere are all rich downland for orchids, especially the Burnt Orchid (*Orchis ustulata*), in both its early and late flowering forms.

The South Downs – North-facing Escarpment

When people picture the South Downs it is this impressive chalk bastion running from the Hampshire border to Beachy Head which comes to mind. Dr.Rose rightly advises us to consider it as a separate ecological entity, since it receives direct sunlight only in the morning and evening, and it is cooler and damper than the south-facing downland slopes.

Extensive ancient grasslands still exist for much of its length, too steep to plough and shaped by generations of grazing sheep. Two orchids are seen at their best on these slopes, the Frog Orchid (*Coeloglossum viride*) and the Musk Orchid (*Herminium monorchis*), but strangely the Man Orchid (*Aceras anthropophorum*) is rare here, although frequent in similar sites in Kent and Surrey. The Marsh Fragrant Orchid (*Gymnadenia conopsea* subsp. *densiflora*) occurs in a number of places on the escarpment, although it is normally to be found in fen habitat.

There is little woodland in the east, but the beech hangers of the West Sussex escarpment are superb for woodland species such as Bird's-nest Orchid and Fly Orchid, the Greater Butterfly-orchid (*Platanthera chlorantha*), the spring-flowering White Helleborine (*Cephalanthera damasonium*) and the late summer-flowering Broad-leaved Helleborine (*Epipactis helleborine*) and Violet Helleborine (*E.purpurata*). They were also the site of the Slender-lipped Helleborine (*Epipactis leptochila*) and the Lady Orchid (*Orchis purpurea*), both of extreme rarity in Sussex, and both unrecorded for the last thirty years.

The Weald of Sussex

This embraces the whole of the county north and east of the chalk outcrop, and is extremely varied in its geology. This is in turn reflected in the species to be found in any particular site.

Wealden woodland in a ghyll at Dallington.

In the east, the once superb shingle beach of the Crumbles between Eastbourne and Pevensey has been ruined by various developments, and the fine colony of the rare Man Orchid (*Aceras anthropophorum*) has been destroyed. Further east, the coastal sands and shingles around Rye hold one consistent colony of the Lizard Orchid (*Himantoglossum hircinum*). In wet hollows there are several colonies of the Marsh Helleborine (*Epipactis palustris*), which has all but vanished from the rest of the county.

The woodlands of the Weald overlying the calcareous sandstone and Weald clay have good populations of the common woodland species, Early-purple Orchid (*Orchis mascula*), Twayblade (*Listera ovata*) and Common Spotted-orchid (*Dactylorhiza fuchsii*), with scattered small populations of Greater Butterfly-orchid (*Platanthera chlorantha*) and Fly Orchid (*Ophrys insectifera*), Broad-leaved Helleborine

(*Epipactis helleborine*) and Violet Helleborine (*E. purpurata*). There still exist some ancient coppiced woodlands, which are potentially good for orchids in the first few years after the coppice is cropped and more sunlight gets in.

The best areas of common-land and heathland, other than Ashdown Forest, all lie in the west of the Weald, but have no particular orchid species except the Heath Spotted-orchid (*Dactylorhiza maculata* subsp. *ericetorum*). Iping, Stedham, Heyshott, Ambersham and Lavington Commons are all superb, but not for orchids. Similarly the wooded ghylls of the High Weald - deep, steep-sided ravines - are fascinating in themselves, but poor in orchid species.

Green-winged Orchid (*Orchis morio*) was widespread until the 1940s on old pastures and meadows on clay soils in the Weald. Nearly all of these meadows have now been 'improved', and the orchid is rare.

Ashdown Forest

Part of the High Weald, it is separated by Dr Rose on account of its distinctive vegetation and historic use. It is high and hilly, overlying the nutrient-poor Ashdown Sand, with areas of open heath and some mature secondary woodland of beech or, in places, of chestnut. The orchid flora of this area is now sadly depleted, but in the past it held good populations of Lesser Butterfly-orchid (*Platanthera bifolia*) and of two nationally rare species now extinct in Sussex. The Small-white Orchid (*Pseudorchis albida*) grew in more than nine places on the Forest, while the Bog Orchid (*Hammarbya paludosa*) similarly was known from some ten sites, but was last seen in 1956. So many of the wet areas have dried out and so many bogs have vanished that there seems little likelihood that it will ever return.

Ashdown Forest near Gill's Lap.

Despite these losses, Ashdown Forest has a healthy population of Heath Spotted-orchids (*Dactylorhiza maculata* subsp. *ericetorum*), a colony of Early Marsh-orchids (*Dactylorhiza incarnata* ssp. *pulchella*) which are now uncommon in Sussex, and a remarkable small colony of the northern form of Fragrant Orchid (*Gymnadenia conopsea* subsp. *borealis*) , which is more commonly associated with the hill pastures of the north of England and Scotland.

In all of Sussex there have been enormous changes since the early days of botanical recording, and particularly in the last sixty years. While we can lament the loss of the countryside under tarmac and houses, not everything is negative. The Great Gale of October 16, 1987 did appalling damage to the trees of East Sussex in particular, but many species of woodland orchids welcomed the increased light afforded by their fallen neighbours, and flowered well in the next few years. Similarly, one old lady now in her 80s remembered the Greater Butterfly-orchid growing in the wood alongside her cottage in her youth, and she would go each spring to admire them. The wood matured, the orchids disappeared and she could find no sign of them - not even a leaf. Then, after a period of nearly 70 years, the wood was clear-felled, and next spring it was full of flowering Butterfly-orchids.

Afforestation is not always bad. Friston Forest in East Sussex was planted with beech and conifers, and now the latter are being cropped and the beech is maturing fast into a rather impressive forest. At the same time the White Helleborine (*Cephalanthera damasonium*) is increasing within the forest, both in total numbers and more importantly by number of sites. One can hope that other woodland orchids will find it to their liking, although it is noteworthy that many of the more common woodland flowers are still absent, giving the feeling that it remains in essence downland covered in trees.

Roads destroy habitat, but at the same time road verges are created as a type of grassland, and with them appear colonies of Common Spotted-orchids (*Dactylorhiza fuchsii*), Bee Orchids (*Ophrys apifera*), Pyramidal Orchids (*Anacamptis pyramidalis*), Early-purple Orchids (*Orchis mascula*) and even Green-winged Orchids (*O. morio*). More important to the state of grassland has been the recession in farming and the consequent decrease in grazing animals, both cattle and sheep. Possibly as a result of this there has been a marked increase of False Brome (*Brachypodium sylvaticum*) and a depression in numbers of downland orchids. However, the failure to graze one downland valley in early spring, as had been the pattern for over 30 years, resulted in the flowering of over 30,000 Green-winged Orchids – an unexpected bonus.

Weather can also have a profound effect on orchid populations. The summer drought of 1976 decimated many populations of Musk Orchids (*Herminium monorchis*). Being shallow-rooted, they literally baked and died. Colonies which habitually held over 10,000 flowering plants were wiped out, and have still not recovered after 25 years.

A roadside verge near Arundel with masses of the Common Spotted-orchid *Dactylorhiza fuchsii*.

Records and Rumours

At the Sussex Biological Recorders Seminar 2000 the point was made that Biodiversity Action Plans (BAPs) depend upon good records of wildlife. The records in their turn depend upon BAPs, for without good conservation action there would be nothing worthwhile to record.

For nearly 250 years botanists have been recording the wild flowers of Sussex, including the orchids, these records giving us a historical perspective by which we hope to judge whether species are thriving or declining. The factors influencing the inevitable changes are many and tend to interact, blurring the interpretation of the effects ascribed to them. Climate, changes in farming and forestry practice, drainage schemes, building development, roads and railways, have all profoundly changed the Sussex which would have been familiar to botanists such as William Borrer, who lived at Henfield in the early nineteenth century.

Records from the 18th and 19th centuries can instil a feeling of gloom for lost glories, but not every change is negative. There are, for instance, increasing populations of orchids on sites such as road verges where an enlightened policy on mowing and the use of herbicides is practised.

The desire to restore what we imagine as the flower-filled meadows of the past is strong. In the late 1950s several national newspapers promoted the idea that everyone should rush out into the countryside, scattering flower seed with gay abandon like latter-day Ceres. Such ideas sent a shudder through those scientifically orientated botanists who had spent years patiently recording the distribution of wildflowers, and from whose data trends in the increase or decrease of those wildflowers could be deduced. Unrecorded 'seeding' would make a mockery of such records. Fortunately the idea died a natural death, but recently there is a move to restore the meadows of the Sussex Weald. In this case the initiative is under the guidance of FWAG (Farming and Wildlife Advisory Group), using native wildflower seed gathered locally under carefully controlled and monitored conditions.

There has been an encouraging increase in meadow creation and arable reversion under the Countryside Stewardship Scheme, and the use of the wildflower seed has been carefully documented, so that proper records are available. This should avoid the mistakes of the past, where seed from European plant populations, genetically and morphologically different from our own, has been sown in a supposed 'restoration' of downland and in the planting of new verges on roads and motorways.

This brings me to the subject of 'odd records'. Orchids, by their very nature, tend to be rare and beautiful, and they therefore attract a disproportionate amount of interest from the general public. Sussex is, after all, the home of the 'Hastings Rarities' – rare birds either seen or shot near Hastings between 1903 and 1919, those killed being preserved by the Hastings taxidermist George Bristow. During the 1960s and 1970s furious debate raged as to their validity, with accusations that they had been collected abroad and brought to Bristow as a lucrative trade. Some, however, have turned up in recent years near Hastings in unimpeachable circumstances.

The temptation exists to introduce a rare orchid, and then 'record' it, and there certainly have been instances of this occurring, although not necessarily in Sussex. In one famous episode Bertoloni's Bee Orchid (*Ophrys bertolonii*) was brought back from the Mediterranean illegally, albeit in all innocence, and planted in a well-known orchid site in Dorset, because it was thought that 'it would be happier there'. The following season it duly flowered and, almost inevitably, was independently discovered by a delighted botanist. The species was accepted on to the British list, and only some time later did someone realise that the soil immediately around it was very different from the site where it grew.

In the past it was the custom to collect and press specimens of wildflowers, which were then assembled in collections – herbaria – on carefully labelled sheets. These gave the origin and date of collection of the flower, and have proved of inestimable historical value. However, one cannot but feel depressed by the sight of a dozen specimens of a rare orchid, now extinct in Sussex, some complete with tubers, and wonder how much collectors contributed to their demise. Herbarium specimens still have a vital part to play in plant recording and taxonomy, but photography by enthusiastic botanists has in large measure come to replace collecting.

Photography in its turn is not without its problems, even if people are careful not to damage or disturb habitat. A herbarium sheet is positive proof that a plant existed – if not necessarily in the place where it was said to have occurred – while the provenance of a photograph is more difficult to establish. In the county which produced the Hastings Rarities and the Piltdown Man, one can be excused for occasionally harbouring healthy suspicions of rarities.

Once in a while truth proves stranger than fiction. For more than a century rumour persisted in Kent that the Military Orchid had grown near Cobham, but no proof existed. In 1998 a herbarium sheet turned up in Bolton Museum bearing a specimen collected in 1836 by Sir Joseph Woods. One of the joys of looking for orchids is that you never know what you may find!

Recently a botanist has adopted the word 'factoid' as a humorous description of records based on rumour or myth which, by constant repetition, have become elevated to the realms of acceptance. The history of orchids in Sussex, as in nearly every part of Britain, is littered with factoids.

We are fortunate in Sussex to possess a highly skilled and active group, the Sussex Botanical Recording Society, whose function is to record the flora of the county. The result of their labours can be seen in the Sussex Plant Atlas (1980 and updates), and will also be an integral part of the botanical Atlas 2000 project covering the entire British Isles. Interesting records, not only of orchids, are always welcome, and if sent to the Biodiversity Records Centre of the Sussex Wildlife Trust at Woods Mill, Henfield, will be passed on to the vice-county recorder concerned. In this way much fascinating information has already been uncovered, in some instances resulting in the protection of rare plants which might otherwise have been inadvertently destroyed. The Sussex Wildlife Trust is extremely active in this field, establishing nature reserves, recording what occurs and working with official bodies such as English Nature and the National Trust to achieve the protection of good sites, wherever this can be done.

Without records there can be no proper conservation.

Sussex Botanologia

Sussex has often benefited from its proximity to London, and inevitably this is true of the historical characters who set the foundations of the botanical knowledge in the county. In the early days some were landed gentry or clerics, while others worked in the City. Most, certainly, were well educated, with both time to spare and active contacts with scientists and fellow botanists in centres of learning in or near London.

In this book I have endeavoured to select those with a particular interest in orchids, and to arrange them in chronological order, although their dates frequently overlap – indeed they were often acquainted with each others' activities. Much can be learned from examining their herbaria, collections of pressed botanical specimens which usually bear the date and place of origin. Many of these sheets, some over 200 years old, are almost artistic in the immaculate way they have been mounted. The labels are in graceful copperplate writing and give us an insight into the minds of those who made them. Some of the sheets have been annotated by later botanists, themselves famous, and their comments can conjure up vivid and often humorous pictures.

I particularly treasure one sheet in the orchid herbarium at Kew, a helleborine which had been collected at West Dean in 1852 by Rev W. Wallinger, as part of the Borrer collection. At the time of its collection the taxonomy of the Epipactis (Helleborine) group had not been clarified and, indeed, it exercises botanical minds to this day. Borrer had titled it *Epipactis latifolia*. At the bottom of the sheet is written 'probably leptochila' C.B.T. (Tahourdin) 14.9.32, and beneath that in tiny neat writing, 'agreed' V.S.S. (Summerhayes) 19.3.1944.

Diagonally there is a third inscription, written so forcefully that the pen nearly penetrates the sheet: 'I disagree – it is vectensis form (ie *E.phyllanthes*) N.B. acuminate leaves with ciliolate edges – subglabrous rachis. D.P. Young.' Dr Young was the doyen of Epipactis taxonomy, and his name is immortalised in *Epipactis youngiana*, a new species discovered in the South Tyne valley in 1976.

Botany can arouse fierce passions!

1666 C. Merrett Orchis Batrachoides autumnalis flore pleno, near Lewes. This is one of the first specific references to an orchid found in Sussex. Wolley-Dod, in the Flora of Sussex, thinks that it is most probably the Frog Orchid (*Coeloglossum viride*).

1696 J. Ray *Synopsis Methodica Stirpium* (2nd edit.)
In Doody's copy (Ca 1706) at the British Museum, there is a manuscript entry of *Malaxis paludosa* (now *Hammarbya paludosa*), the Bog Orchid at 'Hurst Hill, Tunbridge Wells'. On a herbarium sheet at Kew, (H.C.Watson 1804 - 1881) there is a note 'Bog behind the plantation by Broadwater Forest towards Harrison's Rocks. No doubt this was inclosed in Ray's days and in all probability it was his place'.

1746–1862 Rev R.F. Bree (d. London)
He lived in Chichester, collecting plant specimens in Sussex and contributing to Sowerby and Smith's English Botany (1796-1814). He discovered Sword-leaved Helleborine (*Cephalanthera longifolia*) in Goodwood Park in 1826, the specimen residing in Watson's herbarium at Kew.

1776–1864 Sir Joseph Woods (b. Stoke Newington; d. Lewes)
He was of Quaker descent, and practised as an architect in London, moving to Lewes in 1833. He was one of the foremost critical botanists of the early 19th Century, doing pioneer work on the genera *Salicornia* and *Rosa*. He contributed to Sowerby and Smith's English Botany and made extensive herbaria which are lodged at the Natural History Museum and the National Museum of Wales.

The fern *Woodsia* was named in his honour by Robert Brown. He collected and noted many orchids, especially in and around Lewes, and sheets bearing his name appear in other herbaria of the period, as gifts or exchanges with friends.

1781–1862 William Borrer (b. Henfield; d. Henfield)
William Borrer was arguably the greatest Sussex botanist of his day, and one of the leading figures among his famous contemporaries, who esteemed him for his deep knowledge and meticulous attention to detail. He was born in Henfield, but soon afterwards the family moved to Pakyns Manor in Hurstpierpoint, his father – also William – being High Sheriff of Sussex from 1801-1802. This was the time of the Napoleonic War, and young Borrer made frequent journeys on horseback throughout Sussex, assisting his father who was engaged in supplying forage to the troops deployed against an imminent threat of invasion. On these journeys his interest in plants and wildlife was stimulated by what he saw.

In 1805 he was made a Fellow of the Linnean Society, and became a great friend of W.J. Hooker, with whom he travelled to the Scottish Highlands in 1810. He married and moved to a new house at Barrow Hill, Henfield, which had an extensive garden. He met and became close friends with Joseph (later Sir Joseph) Woods, and H.C.Watson.

Borrer travelled extensively, always wanting to see any new plants at first hand, and travelled three times all the way to Westmoreland to an alleged site for the Lady's-slipper Orchid (*Cypripedium calceolus*). This was a spurious site invented by a local guide, who made a good thing by taking botanists to see it, and then being deeply upset by its absence! Over a period of 44 years Borrer added 21 new records to the British flora from sites as far away as Cornwall and Caithness - all this in the 19th Century when travel was far from easy.

He developed a remarkable garden, which contained over six thousand species of plants, some of which escaped and can still to this day be found growing around Henfield. Both the garlics *Allium roseum* and the white-flowered *A.paradoxum* persist as relics of Borrer's garden.

His herbarium is kept at Kew, where many of the Sussex specimens are annotated as being collected for Borrer by J. Weaver, himself a good all-round naturalist, who contributed a large section on natural history to Rev H.D. Gordon's History of Harting (1877). One of Borrer's own collections is of the Early Spider-orchid (*Ophrys sphegodes*) from near Pulborough, labelled as *Ophrys aranifera*.

William Borrer. Drawing by Juliet Pannet from a photograph of a portrait painted in 1847 by an unknown artist. *[Royal Botanic Gardens, Kew]*

1784 G.A. Walpoole
His 'The New British Traveller' (British Museum) contains many new plant records for Sussex, which include the Greater Butterfly-orchid (*Platanthera chlorantha*) and the Green-winged Orchid (*Orchis morio*).

1804–1881 Rev G.E. Smith (b. Camberwell; d. Ockbrook, Derby)
He was curate of Sellinge in Kent from 1830-1832, and then worked in parishes in both Yorkshire and Derbyshire. An indefatigable botanist, he collected and studied plants in both Sussex and Kent, and made the description of *Ophrys sphegodes* for Sowerby and Smith's English Botany. His herbaria are deposited at the Natural History Museum, at Kew and the National Museum of Wales. He lived for many years at Sandgate in Kent, and published the Catalogue of Plants of South Kent.

1804–1881 H.C. Watson
An exact contemporary of Rev G.E.Smith, Watson was also a close friend of William Borrer. His herbarium rests at Kew, an extensive collection from all over Sussex, many of the sheets appearing under his name in Borrer's herbarium.

There are two impressive orchid sheets, one of Small-white Orchid (*Pseudorchis albida*), which is now extinct in Sussex and was collected from near Nutley in both 1840 and 1841, and another of many specimens of Early Spider-orchid (*Ophrys sphegodes*) from Birling Gap in 1837 and Pyecombe in 1859. It has long been gone from the Pyecombe site.

1819–1896 F.C.S. Roper (b. Hackney; d. Eastbourne)
Most of Roper's collections are from East Sussex, as he lived for many years in Eastbourne, where he became President of the Eastbourne Natural History Society. His herbaria are lodged at the Booth Museum in Brighton and at the National Museum of Wales. It is obvious that orchids fascinated him, and there are dozens of sheets of collections, including a depressing number of spikes of *Pseudorchis albida* and Bog Orchid (*Hammarbya paludosa*) from Ashdown Forest.

He also found Sword-leaved Helleborine (*Cephalanthera longifolia*) near Goodwood, and knew it from Lewes, where it was collected for him by J.H.A. Jenner in 1879. He is best remembered for his Flora of Eastbourne (1875) and for a series of notes on the flora of East Sussex published in 1881–82 in the Journal of Botany. He died at Palgrave House in Eastbourne.

1827–1914 Rev E.N. Bloomfield (b. Suffolk; d. Guestling)
He became rector of Guestling in 1862, and collected extensively in the Hastings area. He published annual notes on local fauna and flora of East Sussex in the proceedings of the Hastings Natural History Society (1906-1914).

1831–1906 Rev F.H. Arnold (b. Petworth; d. Emsworth)
Rev Arnold lived at The Hermitage, Westbourne in the extreme west of the county, and this is mirrored in the bias of his collected material, principally from sites in West Sussex. This tended to colour his ideas on plant distribution, with an assumption that circumstances were the same in the east, which was not always the case. He was an extensive correspondent, but was also very active in the field, forming a large herbarium, mainly collected 1875-1887, which was given to Christ's Hospital. It is now in the Booth Museum in Brighton.

He was educated by the Rev Thomas Sockett, rector of Petworth, and surely the 'Sokot' referred to by the botanical illustrator F. Bauer. (See Monkey Orchid in **The Factoid File**, p 124.)

It is highly probable that it was he who sparked the young Arnold's interest in botany. Indeed, they may well have gone together to the site for Bog Orchid (*Hammarbya paludosa*) at Duncton Common in 1853.

Some of his early records include the Frog Orchid (*Coeloglossum viride*) at Goodwood and Harting, and the Sword-leaved Helleborine (*Cephalanthera longifolia*), recorded as *C.ensifolia*.

He is best remembered for his Flora of Sussex, a slim volume published in 1887, with a second edition edited after his death by his daughter Miss M.H. Arnold. This work was very popular, and every Sussex botanist of the early 20th Century had their "Arnold", often heavily annotated with their own records.

1833–1912 Thomas Hilton (b. Brighton; d. Brighton)

From all contemporary reports Thomas Hilton appears to have been a delightful, modest man, with a prodigious self-taught knowledge of botany. His father kept a shop in Church Street, Brighton, where he was born, and apart from some schooling in Croydon he remained there until his retirement in 1900, when he took up botany to occupy his leisure time. He planned to form a collection of fifty species, thinking that would be complete. Shortly before his death he remarked, 'I have got over two thousand, and I have not got them all!'

In 1894 he initiated a regular Exhibition of Wild Flowers in the Museum at the Royal Pavilion, which he provided from May until September. These he often collected personally, and he is known to have walked to Cuckmere Haven and back – a distance of 30 miles – just to provide a flower which someone wished to see.

Thomas Hilton. [Booth Museum of Natural History, Brighton]

From his herbarium sheets one can find that on his many botanical excursions his companions were fellow botanists C.E. Salmon, who wrote the Flora of Surrey (1931), and Rev W.C.Barton, the latter a great friend of the famous taxonomist G.C. Druce.

Hilton formed three large herbaria which are now in the Natural History Museum, the Booth Museum in Brighton and at Kew, and he was for some years the curator of the Brighton Museum. Most of his herbarium sheets date from 1894–1900, and come from all over Sussex.

I was particularly intrigued by his record of the pale-flowered form of the Bee Orchid (*Ophrys apifera* var.*flavescens*), which he found at Beachy Head. This is the first record of the variety in Britain to my knowledge, and it still grows there.

1851–1939 Henry S. Salt (b. India)

H.S. Salt taught at Eton but certainly knew Sussex well, as I have seen from his correspondence with fellow botanist Lady Davy. He contributed many records to Wolley-Dod's Flora of Sussex, and on his own account wrote two books, Call of the Wild Flower (1922) and Our Vanishing Wild Flowers (1928).

He was the last to record Sword-leaved Helleborine (*Cephalanthera longifolia*) at Offham near Lewes between 1923 and 1928, when he recorded 20 flowering spikes. He left a detailed sketch-map of the site, and there are hopes that it may one day reappear under current enlightened woodland management.

1853–1900 J.H.A. Jenner
He lived for most of his life in Battle, botanising mainly in East Sussex, with many records from Hastings, Eastbourne, Beachy Head and Lewes. Among the rare orchids recorded by him there is a sheet of the Lady Orchid (*Orchis purpurea*) from 'near Lewes', where a single plant was found by Herbert Jenner, and the Lizard Orchid (*Himantoglossum hircinum*) from the Cuckmere district 'near Eastbourne', collected by E.J. Bedford. Some of his collections appear in Arnold's herbarium.

He contributed notes on Sussex flora to the Eastbourne Natural History Society 1876–7, and to the Brighton Natural History Society in 1889. His herbaria are lodged at the Natural History Museum and at Kew.

1858–1924 H.L.F. Guermonprez (b. Chelsea; d. Bognor Regis)
Guermonprez was a most remarkable man, whose contribution to the study of natural history in Sussex has been greatly undervalued.

The eldest child of a Belgian emigré, Jean Henri Guermonprez, he moved with his family to Bognor in 1891 – first to Albert Road, and then to a larger house, 'Dalkeith', in the same street. He had qualified as an architect, but appears never to have practised, applying his energy to the study of birds, plants, insects, crustaceans and archaeology. His botanical collection alone contains over 40,000 specimens, and in all this activity he was self-taught.

He made a striking figure, tall and bearded, with a deep but kindly voice, never happier than when imparting his wisdom to budding young naturalists. He could on occasion give vent to sudden bursts of temper, when, according to biographical notes by M.D.Crane, 'He was liable to walk out of the house and disappear for perhaps as much as week at a time, returning tired, dirty and dishevelled.'

Far better is he remembered for his courtesy, and for his generosity in making material and knowledge available to others. One young lady remembers him 'striding over the downs. I was with my father, and Mr. Guermonprez doffed his hat to us, and out fell a bird's nest'.

He frequently took his family out in a two-horse chaise to remote villages such as Graffham and Selham, to look for specimens. 'He taught us to use our eyes,' his son Harry later recalled, 'to see things that other people missed, and through him we learned to see beauty.'

The legacy of these expeditions is the vast collection of exquisite watercolours he painted, now in the Portsmouth City Museum. His sister Harriet was as good an artist, and her work also survives. Unfortunately, however, much of his collection suffered damage, first when 'Dalkeith' was hit by a bomb in February 1943, and from later damage by damp and insect activity, before it finally reached the care of the museum.

Guermonprez took little part in the activities of local natural history societies, but he did correspond particularly with Rev E.N. Bloomfield and C.B. Tahourdin. He also contributed regular 'Selbourne Notes' in the West Sussex Gazette – a series which had previously been in the charge of Rev F.H. Arnold – from 1906 until his death in 1924.

The Portsmouth City Museum has already mounted one exhibition of his work, and it would be a fitting tribute to a man who was known as 'The Gilbert White of Bognor' if a more permanent display were possible.

1867–1954 Rev A.G. Gregor (b. Retford, Notts; d. Worthing)
He was vicar of Firle from 1927 to 1946, and collected extensively in East Sussex, particularly in the Hastings area. There are two large herbaria, at Kew and at the National Museum of Wales, which contain some orchid specimens, and many other herbarium sheets in other collections of the period to which he contributed.

1861–1948 A.H. Wolley-Dod (b. Eton; d. Mayfield)
A.H.Wolley-Dod was regular soldier, reaching the rank of lieutenant-colonel in the Royal Artillery. He served overseas in Africa, Gibraltar and in California, and in each posting he made extensive studies of the local flora. His herbarium is kept at the Natural History Museum, with a few additional sheets in the museum at Tunbridge Wells.

He was an expert in the difficult genus *Rosa*, but is probably best known as the editor of the 1937 Flora of Sussex, a monumental work and a milestone in the history of botany in Sussex.

A.H. Wolley-Dod.
[Courtesy of Hunt Institute for Botanical Documentation, Carnegie Mellon University, Pittsburgh, PA]

1866–1953 E.J. Bedford (b. Lewes ; d. Lewes)
E.J. Bedford was the son of a tax collector. His first teaching post came in 1883 as master of the Brighton School of Art, and then in 1892 as Head Master of the Eastbourne Municipal School of Art and Design. He was a talented botanical artist and painted the artwork for a fine series of postcards of British Orchids published by the then British Museum (Natural History) in the early 1930's and printed by Waterlow and Sons.

In 1901 he moved from Lewes to 'Anderida', 13 Gorringe Road, Eastbourne, to be nearer his work, before returning in the 1920s to Lewes as Principal of the Lewes School of Art.

He was a fine botanist and a keen antiquarian, and from early in his career used photography as a means of recording. His photographs are of the highest quality, such as those taken at the 1891 Lewes Sheep Fair, which display buyers in top hats and frock coats, with shepherds in traditional smocks. He took some superb railway photographs which feature in John Minnis's recent book, and took many black and white photographs of orchids, some of which appear in V.S. Summerhayes' Wild Orchids of Britain.

He was very jealous of his photographs, and made a point of always being present when prints were made from his negatives, so that no unauthorised copies could be made.

He set up the Lewes Borough Museum in the old Market Tower in 1921 – a crowded and damp place by all accounts – before it moved to Albion Street in 1934, and he remained curator until his retirement in 1950. In this position he became the local reference point for many botanists, and his interest in wild orchids meant that many specimens of rare or unusual forms found

E.J. Bedford. [Sussex Archaeological Society]

their way to him for his opinion. Many of his herbarium sheets record visits to orchid sites such as Cooksbridge and Kingston in East Sussex, often in the company of the taxonomist H.W. Pugsley. Bedford was as cagey about botanical sites as he was jealous of his photographs, and he refused to tell any conservation workers the exact location of a plant, even in the strictest confidence. His extreme caution, alas, may have contributed to the loss of the Small-white Orchid (*Pseudorchis albida*) near Nutley.

He published a number of notes, 'On some rare Sussex orchids' (1913), 'On *Orchis hircinum* (sic) in Sussex (near Lewes and elsewhere)' and '*Himantoglossum* (as Orchis) *hircinum* (Lewes)', mainly in the Journal of Botany.

Several dozen photographs were found in the Lewes Photographic Society archive during the 1980s, and these were passed on to me. Many were untitled with no provenance, but I realised that they matched up exactly with the drawings on the famous postcards, and also with photographs which appear in Wolley-Dod's Flora of Sussex, and in Tahourdin's 'Orchid Notes'. In particular there were several pictures of the strange semi-peloric Bee Orchid (*Ophrys apifera*) found near Glynde in 1932 by Kathleen Pickard, and of the Lizard Orchid (*Himantoglossum hircinum*) found near Plumpton in 1920. These photographs have been re-united with their companion watercolours at the Natural History Museum. His herbarium is kept at Kew.

He spent his last years at 11 St John's Terrace, Lewes, where his death is recorded in rather bizarre circumstances. On February 6, 1953 police forced an entry, finding him dead on the upstairs landing and his housekeeper, Miss Flora Barden, dead in the downstairs kitchen. It was a sad end to a highly talented man who had contributed so widely at a high level of excellence.

1870–1946 Rev A.A. Evans (d. Chichester)
He was ordained in Durham in 1891, and held curacies in Durham, Leicestershire and Yorkshire, before moving to Sussex in 1897. In biographical notes compiled in 1998 by Frances Abraham, she notes curacies in 'Framfield (1897-99), Arundel (1899-1900), Slinfold (1901-02), Clapham and Patching (1902-04) and Pevensey (1904-08)'. After this restless career, he was vicar of East Dean with Friston from 1908 to 1929, retiring to live in Chichester.

His herbarium at Kew contains several sheets of orchid specimens from the Beachy Head area, and one of the Lizard Orchid (*Himantoglossum hircinum*) from Polegate in 1914.

He contributed 'A Countryman's Diary' regularly to the Sussex County Magazine in the 1920s and 1930s, and wrote at least three books on the Sussex countryside. As with Rev A.G. Gregor, material supplied by him appears on herbarium sheets in other collections.

1878–1956 B.T.Lowne (b. Finchley; d. Worthing)
An almost exact contemporary of Rev Gregor, he was an electrical engineer and an excellent amateur botanist. His herbarium material is kept at Kew, with several sheets in the general orchid herbarium.

18??–19?? C.B. Tahourdin (d. Wallington, Surrey)
Tahourdin was a solicitor, an expert on native British orchids, a talented botanical artist and photographer. He published a number of yearly booklets on current matters of interest to orchid specialists, and wrote The Native Orchids of Britain (1925). He collected widely, corresponded with Gregor, Evans, Bedford, Wolley-Dod and many others, and was responsible for sorting out the *Orchidaceae* for the 1937 Flora of Sussex.

His herbarium is kept at Reading University, and includes a sheet of the semi-peloric Bee Orchid (*Ophrys apifera*) from Glynde, dated 21.6.1926.

1897–1974 V.S. Summerhayes (b. Street, Somerset ; d. Sidmouth, Devon)
By all accounts V.S. Summerhayes was a kindly, happy man, with an enormous capacity for work, in which his scrupulously unbiased scientific approach brought him international renown in the orchid world.

He was born in Somerset in the town of Street, hard by ancient Glastonbury. Both his father and grandfather worked for C. and J. Clark's, nurserymen. One of the founders of Clark's kept a detailed diary of botanical observations made in the area, so it was not surprising that this became his life interest. He was educated at Sexey's Boys School in Bruton, where he had some excellent botany teachers who furthered his interest in plant science. As with so many of his generation, his life was interrupted by service in the First World War, where he served in the Royal Engineers.

During his university career he came under the influence of many famous botanists including Marie Stopes. He took part in the 1921 Oxford University Expedition to Spitzbergen, which stimulated his other lifelong interest, in ecology, which at that time was just becoming an acceptable scientific discipline in Britain. He joined Kew in 1924, and was soon put in charge of the orchid herbarium and the Australian and Polynesian section, retiring as Principal Scientific Officer in 1964.

V.S. Summerhayes. [Watsonia]

He published extensively on the African orchid flora, but to the general public he is probably best known as the author of Wild Orchids of Britain, published by Collins in the New Naturalist series in 1951. John Gilmour was one of the editors, and had been a colleague in his early days at Kew. Even after the passage of half a century it is easy to appreciate the impressive scholarship of this book, with colour photographs taken by Robert Atkinson which set a benchmark by which others could be judged. It was justly a bestseller.

He acted for many years as referee for the Botanical Society of the British Isles in determining difficult orchid species, and took a particular interest in the genus *Dactylorhiza*.

He certainly visited orchid sites in Sussex on many occasions, with E.J. Bedford, Ted Lousley, Francis Rose and C.B. Tahourdin. They appear to have had a field day, in all senses of the word, at a Marsh-orchid site near Lewes, as several herbarium sheets at Kew, Reading University and the Natural History Museum bear witness – all neatly inscribed with the tiny initials VSS.

He was awarded the OBE in 1960 for his services to taxonomy, and the Malayan Orchid Society Gold Medal in 1963. At the time of his death he was preparing another illustrated handbook on British orchids.

1898–1949 Phyllis Stockdale (b. London; d. Eastbourne)
The first part of her life was spent in East Grinstead, where her father was a baker and confectioner, with a love of flowers and gardens. She worked in Barclays Bank, where she met her husband Reginald Horrill, and on his promotion they moved to Willingdon near Eastbourne. There were many botanical outings to downs and marshes, collecting plants which she often

painted. Her children remember going out on to the downs with their mother and grandfather to collect orchids in a small black vasculum.

Her herbarium is kept at Bexhill Museum. She was closely involved with the 1937 Flora of Sussex, as shown by a comparison of her material with the notes and records in Wolley-Dod. Sadly there are no orchid specimens in the collection, nor any of her watercolour drawings.

(Dates unknown) F.F. Woods

Frederick Woods was well known as 'The Ditchling Naturalist', keeping a small museum in the village. He was Bailiff of Ditchling Common, where he worked at St George's Retreat, and he published Round About Sussex Downs in 1925.

He certainly contributed specimens and data to botanists at the time – there is a herbarium sheet of Marsh Helleborine (*Epipactis palustris*) collected by him for C.B. Tahourdin in 1926 (Reading University) – but he seems to have been a somewhat crusty character, and in the preface to the Flora of Sussex Wolley-Dod observes that 'his list of species contains so many doubtful records, unconfirmed elsewhere, that little use has been made of it'.

Despite this stricture, some of the 'doubtful records' have in fact been verified later, which makes one mindful of the ornithological Hastings Rarities.

1898–1981 Maj W.W.Phillips (d. Bognor)

Maj Phillips' interest in natural history arose under unusual circumstances as a prisoner of war of the Turks during the First World War. He was captured in April 1916 at Kut-el-Amara, and to while away the tedium of incarceration he started to study the fauna and flora.

After the war he underwent medical treatment at the sanitorium of the King Edward VII Hospital north of Midhurst, and his annotated 'Arnold', although undated, contains numerous botanical records of the immediate area.

He then went to live in Easebourne, before going to Ceylon as a tea-planter after his Army service. He rapidly became an authority on the birds and mammals of Ceylon, where he also worked for the Ceylon Game and Fauna Protection Society, and his book The Mammals of Ceylon is a standard reference work.

Maj W.W. Phillips.

He was an expert on bats, and on his return to Britain recorded the Mouse-eared Bat at its then only known British location in Singleton.

He was deeply interested in botany, recording the Sword-leaved Helleborine (*Cephalanthera longifolia*) at Goodwood in 1970 and at Westdean, and discovered a colony of Southern Marsh-orchid (*Dactylorhiza praetermissa*) at the east end of Pagham Lagoon, persuading the West Sussex County Council to incorporate the small area into the Local Nature Reserve.

He was co-author of the Natural History of Pagham Harbour (1979) and wrote a Jubilee Booklet on the natural history of Aldwick Bay Estate, Bognor Regis, where he had moved on retirement. He made extensive herbaria which are now at Kew and the Natural History Museum, as well as collections in the Museum of Colombo, Ceylon.

1903–1999 Kathleen N.I. Pickard-Smith (b. Glynde; d. Glynde)
Katie was born in the old farmhouse of the Glynde Estate, the daughter of Tom Pickard, the redoubtable Steward of Glynde. By all accounts - and there are many - Tom was a formidable character, and his daughter inherited much of that spirit. Never one to suffer fools gladly, Katie was a warm-hearted and generous friend to many in the worlds of botany and horticulture.

She trained as a musician, and ran the Brighton Music school, which in those days resided in the old Aeolian Hall. Throughout her life she botanised extensively, especially in East Sussex. Many of the records, including those of the Lizard Orchid and the unique semi-peloric Bee Orchid, whose photograph by E.J. Bedford appears at the back of the Flora of Sussex, were her discoveries. I have a letter written to her by H.S.Salt in 1926, thanking her for instructions for finding the tiny Hare's-ear (*Bupleurum baldense*): 'I doubt if I could have found it without your directions.'

She was a founder member in 1962 of the Alpine Garden Society, and her apparently chaotic garden was a treasure house of rare and unusual plants which thrived under her skilled care.

Her other skill was in the keeping and rearing of reptiles. Her book Living with Reptiles remains one of the best practical guides to keeping reptiles well, and, above all, contented. Those of us who visited her remember her best by the iguanas which lived around the house. One particularly huge and long-lived 'Iggy' resided along the top of a bookcase, his favourite spot under a warm lamp. Many visitors thought he was stuffed, and Katie lost a number of sherry glasses which dropped from the nerveless fingers of guests, who suddenly found themselves regarded by an extremely lively basilisk stare!

Elizabeth Strangman recounts a typical story of Katie. At a meeting of the AGS at Vincent Square in London, she found her in the ladies' toilet, with a load of tiny terrapins swimming in the hand basin. These she proceeded to dry off and pop into her bra, explaining that it was far too hot to have left them at home!

Many of us cherish the memory of a superb field botanist, with a mind like a razor even in old age, and a kindly but wicked wit.

1903–1989 O. Buckle (d. Worthing)
Oliver Buckle had his interest in flowers stimulated at an early age by his father, who took him on country walks. This interest became in later life a consuming passion, which was not always appreciated fully by his family. He worked with the Midland Bank for 45 years, the last 17 years as manager in Worthing, and was the first honorary treasurer for the Sussex Wildlife Trust.

He was a very positive character with a marvellous turn of phrase, and for more than 50 years he ran a very popular series of classes in field botany for the Workers' Educational Association at Newlyn Place, Worthing. He was a marvellous teacher, having endless patience, and his lectures were remembered for the many good tips for distinguishing closely related species. He was also knowledgeable on the uses of plants, and on the legends associated with them.

He was the last person, in 1952, to record the Bog Orchid (*Hammarbya paludosa*) on Ashdown Forest, and the Lady Orchid (*Orchis purpurea*) at Chanctonbury. The BSBI Recorder for West Sussex for some years, he was also the first director of the Sussex Flora Committee.

Francis Rose was told by Oliver that, when trespassing in pursuit of a plant, he often put on a clerical dog-collar, which worked wonders in allowing access by suspicious land-owners. He had a great interest in the genus *Arum*, and also in alpines, on which there is a cautionary tale for all botanists. Bending down to take a closer look at an interesting flower, he slipped and fell nearly 600m. Despite various fractures and a short stay in hospital, he managed, while being carried on a stretcher, to spot *Erigeron mucronatus* at Milan Airport when he was flown home.

1907–1976 J.E. Lousley (b. Clapham; d. Streatham Common)
Ted Lousley's family were Berkshire farmers, his great-grandfather Job Lousley (1790-1855) making a substantial herbarium collection of local plants in the Newbury area, the sheets being kept with Ted Lousley's own herbarium at Reading University.

However, Ted's father Jethro had no great love of farming and came to work in London, where J. Edward was born and brought up. At the age of 12 he attended the Strand School in Brixton, and was taken on botanical outings by W.R. Sherrin, the curator of the South London Botanical Institute. These bicycle expeditions founded his abiding love of the Surrey countryside.

Ted Lousley started work in 1924 with Barclays Bank in south London, staying with the bank until his retirement in 1967 as departmental manager of the trustee department at head office. Despite the pressures of professional life, he was a passionate field botanist from the start, and made innumerable expeditions by public transport to every part of the British Isles, expeditions planned in meticulous detail to maximise the potential for plant finding that the time allowed.

It was no surprise that the attention to detail that his professional life demanded spilled over into his hobby, his herbarium becoming the largest in private ownership, all controlled by a vast card index system: no computers in those days.

The card index collection makes a fascinating study, made even more intriguing by the annotations and comments scribbled round the margins – comments unfailingly interesting and often highly amusing, especially those about other botanists.

J.E. Lousley at Wicken Fen, 1960. [Watsonia]

He worked in particular on the difficult genus *Rumex* (Docks), a subject on which his knowledge was internationally recognised.

One of the best remembered episodes was his rediscovery in 1947 of the Military Orchid (*Orchis militaris*) at Homefield Wood in Buckinghamshire. Ted was very cagey about releasing details of its whereabouts, which only served to stimulate his friends in their own search. By sheer persistence they eventually found the site, leading to the dispatch of the notorious telegram: 'The Soldiers are at home in their field.'

Ted Lousley is probably best remembered by his very fine book Wild Flowers of Chalk and Limestone (1950 Collins New Naturalist series), which was based to a large extent on years of study on Box Hill in his beloved Surrey. He also worked for over 40 years on the Flora of the Isles of Scilly (1971), work which he had almost completed before the outbreak of the second world war. After the war he took a particular interest in the explosion of wild flowers and aliens appearing in the bombed sites all over London, and on which once again he became an authority.

Ted Lousley was heavily involved with the South London Botanical Institute from an early age, and soon was contributing records which caused what J.G. Dony referred to as minor crisis. Records were always listed under the initials of the finder (J.E.L), much to the annoyance of an elderly and distinguished member, J.E. Little, who found his records credited to the young enthusiast. He then joined the Botanical Society and Exchange Club, and ultimately the newly formed Botanical Society of the British Isles. His commercial wisdom, as well as his botanical expertise, were of immeasurable value in making the society the vibrant body it is today, and he served as its president from 1961 to 1965.

He was also chairman of the BSBI maps committee from 1950 onwards, enlisting the help of about 1500 amateur and professional botanists, and collating 1.5 million records, which bore fruit in the 1962 Atlas of the British Flora. He was also deeply committed to nature conservation, becoming the first honorary secretary of the Council for Nature. In this role he was very active in the fight to save Upper Teesdale from inundation.

The sheer volume of excellence is astonishing, considering that Ted Lousley led a busy and demanding professional life at the same time. His huge herbarium is deposited at Reading University, and contains a number of sheets of Sussex orchids. He certainly knew Sussex well, and Mary Briggs remembers an outing to Amberley Wild Brooks where the Southern Marsh-orchid (*Dactylorhiza praetermissa*) was discovered.

The picture is of an industrious and painstaking botanist, well deserving the high esteem in which he was held by his many friends. Although not a Sussex man, Ted Lousley made a profound impression on Sussex botany and a whole generation of Sussex botanists. Sadly he never saw the completion of his Flora of Surrey, on which he was working at the time of his death.

1909–1986 E.C.Wallace (b. Blackfriars, London d. Sutton, Surrey)
Ted Wallace moved with his family to Surrey at the age of two, and lived all his life in the same house. His father had no sympathy with his botanical interests, although his mother was more encouraging. Like Ted Lousley, he was fortunate to come to the notice of W.R. Sherring of the South London Botanical Institute, who greatly encouraged him.

He worked for W.H. Smith all his life, except for war service in the RAF as a medical orderly, but found time to botanise widely in Surrey, Sussex, Hampshire and Kent, and spent many summer holidays in Scotland. Francis Rose recalls a trip to the then scarcely explored area of Knoydart in Westerness, where they camped in a disused shepherd's hut, plagued by ticks during the day and by bed-bugs at night. He also made many botanical trips abroad to Japan, Kashmir, Florida, Alaska, Canada and Australia, as well as to Europe.

His main interest was in bryophytes, on which he was a world expert, and he loved sedges, too. He joined the Botanical Society of the British Isles in 1932, becoming vice-president, and for years acted as archivist for the BSBI and as Recorder for West Sussex. He made widespread collections, especially in West Sussex. Many trips were made in the company of his friend Ted Lousley, and several sheets of Sussex orchids carry both their names.

Ted Wallace compiled a huge herbarium, which is divided between the University of Reading, Aberdeen, the Royal Botanic Garden Edinburgh and the National Museum of Wales.

He was a kind and gentle man with a quiet sense of humour, patient with young botanitsts anxious to learn, and armed with a prodigious memory for both plants and locations. Mary Briggs remembers being taken with unerring precision to see a plant which Ted had last seen at a site 30 years before.

Ted Wallace and *Carex illegitima*.

His last trip was to Rhodes in 1986, where he was able to see the rare sedge *Carex illegitima*, which he had much wanted to find. Mary Briggs' photograph of his happy smile (*see facing page*) encapsulates the joy of a botanist successful in his quest.

19??–1978 Ian Frenguelli (d. Seychelles)
Ian was one of those quiet people who did a great deal for Sussex botany, but never raised a high profile. For some years he operated Warwick Nursery at Eastergate, and then worked for Farmers and Growers Industries. He is remembered as an enthusiastic and most charming man.

He did a great deal as Recorder for West Sussex for the flora committee from 1967 to 1977, despite continuing illness. Frank Penfold recalls going with him in May 1971 to see the Sword-leaved Helleborine.

Ian died in the Seychelles on New Year's day 1978 while on holiday, and is buried on La Digue under a great mango tree.

1917–1972 D.P. Young
Dr Donald Young had a distinguished career as a research chemist, working first for British Celanese Ltd and then for the Distillers Company, where he was a senior research chemist until his retirement.

His other skill was as a systemic botanist, where he was the acknowledged expert on the genus *Epipactis* (Helleborines) and on *Oxalis* (Sorrels). His was the impassioned comment on the 1852 Borrer herbarium *Epipactis* specimen collected at West Dean (*see page 13*).

He joined the Botanical Society of the British Isles in 1945, and for many years acted as referee for the genus *Epipactis*, so that his judgement was sought on the rare helleborines *E.leptochila* and *E.phyllanthes* from West Sussex. The new species discovered in 1976 in the South Tyne valley by John Richards was named *Epipactis youngiana* in his honour.

D.P Young.

Donald Young was born with severe spinal curvature, over which he triumphed with great and improbable courage, climbing mountains and driving a fast sports car. Despite his inevitable shyness, he was always ready to assist anyone in any way he could, and was a kindly man with a strong sense of humour.

19??–1998 Ceres Esplan
Ceres Esplan was probably best known under her author's 'nom de plume' of Alison Ross. For many years she contributed a popular weekly column of nature notes to the *West Sussex Gazette* and the *Worthing Herald*.

She wrote Plant Hunting in Sussex for *The Field* in 1949, and An Inch and Under for the same publication in 1958. There were also natural history books for children, and the foreword to the Sussex Plant Atlas of 1980.

She recalled her first flower memory as being shown a Bee Orchid at Cissbury Hill at the age of five, and was fortunate enough to see the Lizard Orchid (*Himantoglossum hircinum*) in Arundel Park and at Bignor – sites at which it did not persist.

After the family moved from Horsham to Amberley in 1950, she became an authority on the plants of Amberley Wild Brooks.

So far Botanologia has told the story of past botanists, all of whom have played a part in the understanding and recording of Sussex orchids. I hope I may be forgiven for finishing this section with a homage to two who are happily still with us, but whose contribution to the Sussex scene is so important a part of the present picture that I should feel it incomplete without them.

Breda Burt

For many years any enquiries concerning plants in East Sussex would be met with the reply: 'Ask Breda. She'll be able to tell you!' As Recorder for East Sussex she exercised a wonderfully benign influence over the vice-county, founded on sheer hard work and attention to detail, backed up by her husband Ernie, who was the support man.

They lived at Boonsfield Farm at Playden, near Rye, where Ernie was born and where they farmed sheep. Friends recall that Breda used to work with books and botanical specimens on a tray while waiting for Ernie to come in from the farm for meals. As soon as he returned she would lift the tray away and proceed with lunch. After retirement Ernie became the photographer half of the botanical partnership.

Mary Briggs recalls the story of their recording quadrats around Camber Castle in 1981 at the request of English Nature – rather a tedious task. It was Ernie who, at the end of a tiring day, suggested 'just one more throw' of the quadrat frame, leading to the rediscovery of Clustered Clover (*Trifolium glomeratum*) which had been thought extinct in Sussex since 1902.

It was always stimulating to be out with Breda on botanical forays. The enthusiasm became infectious, and I well remember visiting the Lizard Orchid (*Himantoglossum hircinum*) and the Marsh Helleborine (*Epipactis palustris*) in her company.

In 1996 Breda and Ernie left Sussex to live nearer family in Worcestershire where, sadly, Ernie died in 1999. They made a great contribution to Sussex botany and to the study of its orchids, and their warm hospitality will long be remembered.

Francis Rose

My first recollection of meeting Francis is over 50 years ago, when he came – I believe on a vast black motorbike – to lecture to our fledgling natural history society at Tonbridge School. At that time he and his wife Wendy were living at West Malling. I was then a very keen birdwatcher, not terribly interested in botany, and I owe my passion for orchids entirely to Francis and the biology master Lyn Thomas. The Kent Field Club, precursor to the Kent Naturalists' Trust, was then in its infancy, and I was encouraged to join – intrigued also by Francis's paper on the Lady Orchid (*Orchis purpurea*) published that year in the Journal of Ecology. Botany was fun!

Francis's own interest in the subject was fostered first by country walks with his naturalist grandfather. This went on to become a profession, teaching first in the botany department at Bedford College and later as Reader in Plant Geography at Kings College, London, from which post he retired – if that is the right word – in 1981. He remains incredibly busy.

Over the years he compiled 200 field note books, starting in 1944, with an estimated 250,000 individual records, and it is this wide personal field experience from all over the British Isles which places him in the forefront of present day botanists. With this goes a passion for conservation based on sound ecological principles and field knowledge.

Dr David Streeter writes: 'It has been given to few botanists the reputation of becoming a legend in their own life-time. Students of behavioural ecology have noted that his dedication to field work has led to a number of characteristic idiosyncratic behavioural responses to adverse working conditions: a deluge of rain merely results in the inversion of his pipe, and failing light brings out the matches.'

Dr Francis Rose: unrivalled knowledge and irrepressible enthusiasm.

At one time Francis possessed a Skoda of dubious mechanical quality. On a botanical trip to the New Forest with a student on board he observed, with typical quiet scientific detachment, that someone had lost a wheel – which was, indeed, to be seen trundling down the road. This was followed fairly rapidly by the subsidence of the Skoda.

I treasure a number of incredibly tatty old one-inch Ordnance Survey maps annotated by him with sites of orchids in Kent, Sussex, Wales and Scotland, but Dr Rose's interests and expertise extend much further than this, to cover all flowering plants, ferns, bryophytes and lichens.

He published the Wild Flower Key in 1981 (Frederick Warne) followed in 1989 by The Colour Identification to the Grasses, Sedges, Rushes and Ferns, and he is the co-author of the Flora of Hampshire.

In all the years Sussex botanists have benefited from his kindly wisdom, and although he started in Kent and now lives in Hampshire, we in Sussex rather like to claim a proprietorial interest. It was with special pleasure that we greeted the news that he had been awarded the MBE.

I cannot do better than conclude with the last paragraph of David Streeter's article on Francis in Watsonia on the occasion when he became an honorary member of the Botanical Society of the British Isles: 'His unrivalled knowledge, irrepressible enthusiasm and ability to make even the commonplace exciting, stimulates all who share his company in the field. And all those privileged to have had their own stirrings of botanical interest fostered by one of the most remarkable botanists of his generation would wish to take this opportunity to say quite simply, "Francis, thank you!"'

Surely this is what we treasure in the memory of those who have helped to build Sussex botany as it is today. We share their knowledge, enthusiasm and warmth, and we stand in their debt.

Botanicus prostratus **– the end of a hard day in the field.**

The Structure of Orchid Flowers

All orchids belong to the Class of Monocotyledons, the young plants emerging from the seeds having a single juvenile leaf or cotyledon, unlike those of many familiar garden plants such as the cabbage, which bear two juvenile leaves and belong to the Class of Dicotyledons.

Members of the Family Orchidaceae are perennial, with fleshy roots or tubers, and unstalked, undivided leaves which are often long and narrow, somewhat fleshy and with parallel veins. The Bird's-nest Orchid (*Neottia nidus-avis*) is unusual in having no proper leaves, these being reduced to sheathing scales at the base of the stem.

The flowers of our native orchids may be born singly or in a spike on an always unbranched stem. They are often apparently complex and brightly coloured, the floral parts not clearly divided into green sepals and coloured petals, but being similar in structure. It is simpler to refer to them as perianth segments, the six members divided into two groups of three, the outer and inner perianth segments. The ventral inner perianth segment is often large and prominent, and is called the labellum or lip.

In some species the base of the labellum is hollowed out to form a backwardly projecting spur, which in the Butterfly Orchid (*Platanthera chlorantha*) is particularly long, elegant and full of nectar. In primitive orchids the labellum develops at the top of the flower. In most of the species occurring in Sussex it has come to lie ventrally, since in the developing flower the ovary twists through 180°. However, in the Bog Orchid (*Hammarbya paludosa*) the labellum occupies the primitive dorsal position, as the flower has rotated through a full 360°: the flower thus appears to be upside down.

The reproductive organs are carried on a common structure called the column, the single stamen divided into two pollen-bearing structures called the pollinia. The pollinia are formed of granular pollen masses borne on a stalk called a caudicle, and attached at their bases by sticky discs called viscidia. It is these which adhere to visiting insects, and which are carried off to allow

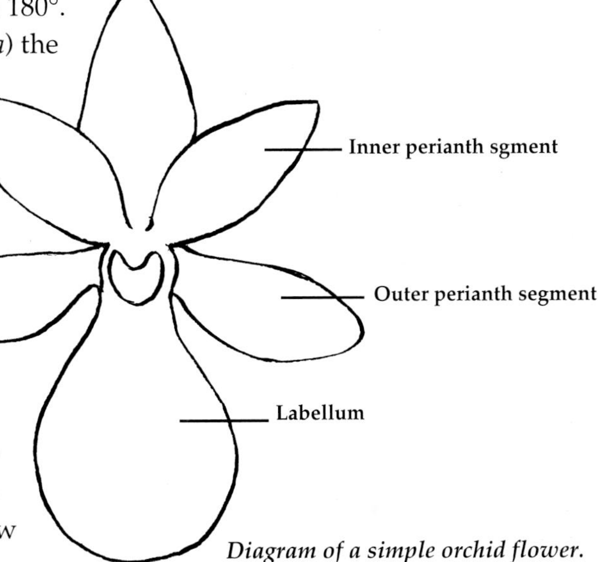

Diagram of a simple orchid flower.

cross-pollination. There are three stigmas, the central sterile stigma forming the beak-like rostellum, with a fertile stigma lying on each side. In many of our orchids the upper perianth segments lie close together, forming a protective hood over the reproductive organs.

The ovary lies between the base of the perianth segments and the stem and often bears a small leaf-like bract at its base. Each ovary is constructed of three compartments, and when ripe the sides split open as three valves, allowing the numerous dust-like seeds to escape.

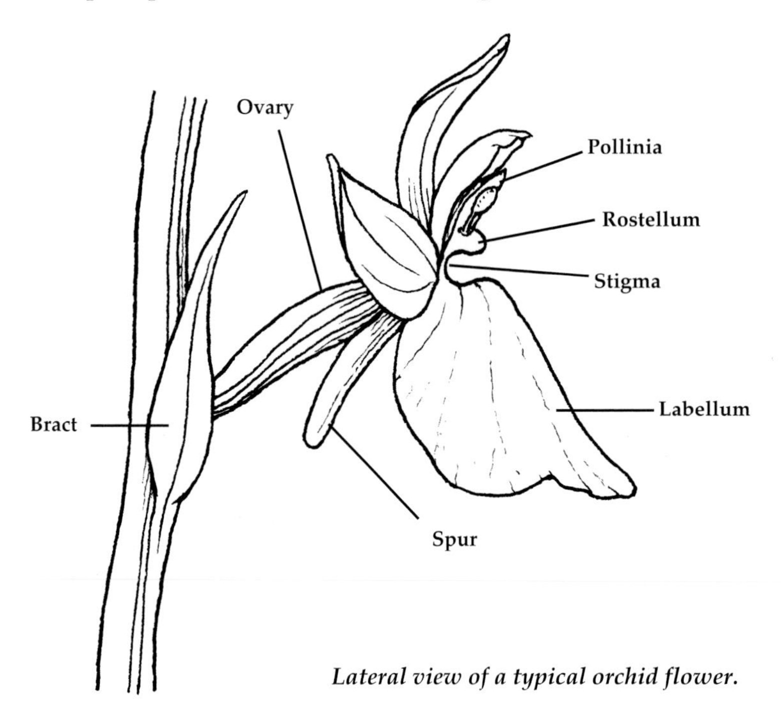

Lateral view of a typical orchid flower.

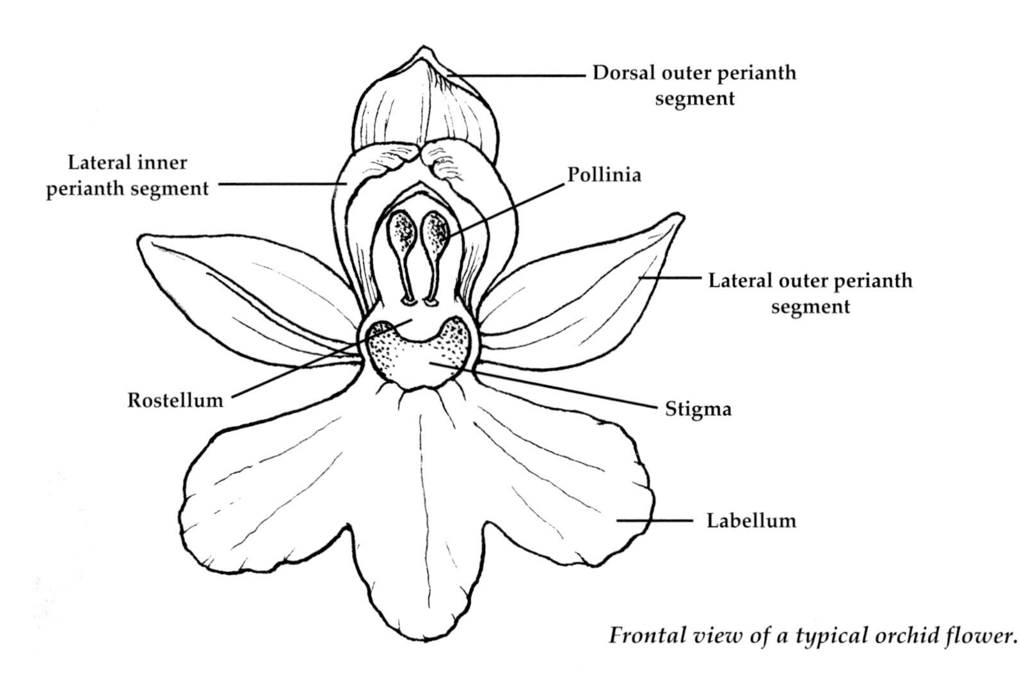

Frontal view of a typical orchid flower.

Germination and Growth

Orchid seeds are minute, 0.1-0.25mm long, and therefore carry very little in the way of food reserves to feed the developing embryo. Climatic conditions must be ideal for the seed to have any chance of successful germination, and in most cases further growth can be assured only if the seed is infected by a mycorrhizal fungus.

It was Noel Bernard (1874-1911) who discovered the role of these fungi, which belong mainly to the genus *Rhizoctonia*. The role of the fungus is complex, since it starts by acting as a parasite and attacking the growing orchid. The orchid then checks it and digests it, gaining nutrients which the fungus has converted from organic humus, a process the young orchid plant is incapable of performing for itself. At certain seasons the orchid will have the upper hand, while in autumn and winter the fungus will thrive, so that the process is neither one of true parasitism, nor of symbiosis (two organisms existing together to their mutual benefit).

Some orchids will throw off the mycorrhizal infection as they mature, while other species, which include the Bird's-nest Orchid and most of the helleborines, are dependent upon the mycorrhizum for their entire lives.

Some orchids are saprophytic, deriving all their nourishment from the breakdown of organic material and not using photosynthesis. This is the process in green plants, which fix the sun's energy through the medium of the pigment chlorophyll. The Bird's-nest Orchid (*Neottia nidus-avis*) is entirely saprophytic, having no chlorophyll and, indeed, no leaves. Instead it has a dense mass of short fleshy roots, heavily infected with mycorrhizal fungus, which resemble a badly made bird's nest and give the orchid its common name.

The first structure formed by the germinating seed is a peg-like protocorm, which has a bud at one end and tiny rootlets. This produces tubers or fibrous roots and the first leaf, at which stage the protocorm withers away. The whole process is very slow and leaves may not be produced for several years. Some species such as the spotted orchids, marsh orchids and Green-winged Orchid will flower in three or four years from seed, while others, such as the Burnt Orchid (*Orchis ustulata*) can take upwards of fifteen years before they mature.

Recent work by scientists has shown that our understanding of this process has not always been accurate. For example, the Early Spider-orchid (*Ophrys sphegodes*) regularly reaches the flowering stage in three years, and not seven or eight years as had long been accepted, and even slow developers such as the Autumn Lady's-tresses (*Spiranthes spiralis*) may flower in four years under laboratory conditions. Knowing accurately the length of the flowering cycle of orchids is very important when planning conservation management, such as deciding in which seasons to cut or graze a site to increase the orchids present.

Orchids are perennials and have adapted to the harsh conditions of winter by dying back to an underground tuber or root system. Each spring fresh leaves emerge and growth resumes. In two downland species, the Bee Orchid (*Ophrys apifera*) and Autumn Lady's-tresses, the fresh leaves form in autumn and overwinter. This accounts for the often frost-scorched or tattered tips of Bee Orchid leaves. The leaf crown of Autumn Lady's-tresses actually develops a year ahead of the flowering spike. A close examination of the flowering plant will reveal no leaves at the base of the stem, but alongside will be the leaf crown from which next year's flower will arise.

Many orchids are monocarpic – they flower once and then die. Careful recording of individual plants has again challenged our preconceived ideas. Although Bee Orchids are usually monocarpic, individual plants have been known to flower for more than eight consecutive years. It is also clear that within a colony of orchid plants there are many mature individuals which may not flower for some years.

Even more perplexing is the manner in which obviously mature plants will suddenly 'appear', as described *(p. 7)* in **Orchid Habitats in Sussex**. The hundreds of flowering Greater Butterfly-orchids could not have grown from seed in one year, and the observer had looked for them for many years without spotting a single leaf in the wood which had been felled. She was both sharp-eyed and an experienced botanist. They must have been existing in a state below ground which enabled them to respond rapidly to the change in local conditions, especially the increased light. Such underground systems are well documented in species like the Ghost Orchid (*Epipogium aphyllum*), which has not yet been found in Sussex. I have found the knobbly, coral-like rhizomes over 100m from the nearest recorded flowering spike, so the unseen underground system must be immense.

Some orchid species are capable of vegetative multiplication. Both *Orchis* and *Ophrys* species may form two tubers in particularly favourable years, giving rise to the formation of clumps of individual plants. The Musk Orchid (*Herminium monorchis*) develops new tubers on the end of stolons or runners, so that satellite individuals appear around the parent plant. These stolons are quite shallow in the soil and are particularly susceptible to dessication, so that the drought of 1976 destroyed many Musk Orchids, although many populations have recovered to some extent.

The Common Twayblade (*Listera ovata*) produces buds on a branching root system, so the satellite plants appear in lines radiating from the parent, growing rapidly to flowering maturity. Growth from seed takes many times as long, so the vegetative process is highly efficient.

The Early-purple Orchid is common in Sussex woods and meadows.

Sexual Reproduction

In 1877 Charles Darwin published his famous paper The Various Contrivances by which Orchids are Fertilised by Insects, the result of many years study of a subject which clearly intrigued him. Darwin's Bank at Downe in north-west Kent, the downland area where many of his field observations were made, is now a flourishing nature reserve under the care of the Kent Wildlife Trust.

Darwin found that although some orchids attract insects by the reward of nectar, many operate a system of deceit, either by mimicry – resembling another individual of the same insect species - or by secreting chemicals called pheromones, which act as sexual attractants.
The pollen of orchids is not wind dispersed, since the granules are sticky and massed together in the pollinia.

The mechanism of insect pollination is easily demonstrated by examining the flower of the Early-purple Orchid (*Orchis mascula*). The two pollinia are separate, each with its own sticky viscidium, and lie on either side of the rostellum, protected by a small flap called the bursicle which prevents them from drying out prematurely.

Bees are attracted to the flowers by a fluid secretion in the wall of the spur, and push their heads into the base of the flower, displacing the bursicles and allowing one or both of the viscidia to adhere to the bee's head or thorax. Within a minute the cells on one side of the caudicle shrink, causing the pollinia to pivot forward through 90^0 so that they project over the head of the bee and can contact the stigma. The time lapse ensures that the bee has in all likelihood moved on to another plant, so that cross-pollination can occur.

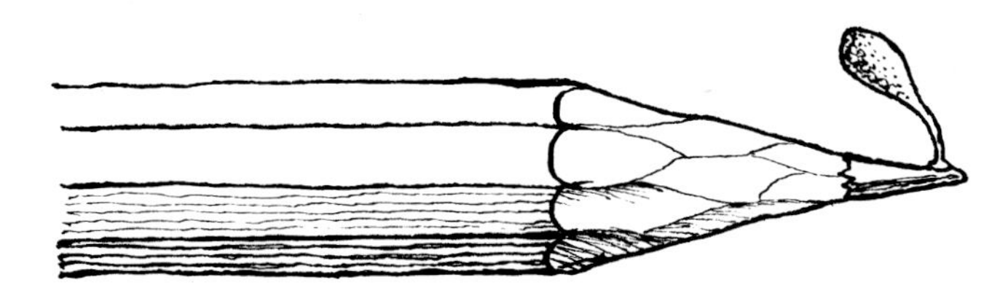

Detached pollinia.

A simple experiment with a pencil point inserted into the flower *(left)* will demonstrate the phenomenon.

The pollinia of the Pyramidal Orchid (*Anacamptis pyramidalis*) and several other long-spurred, nectar secreting orchids show a further refinement. Fertilisation is effected by moths and butterflies, which have to insert their long proboscis down into the spur to reach the nectar. The two pollinia arise from one viscidium, which rolls round when detached and grips the proboscis firmly so that it cannot be dislodged. In this case the pollinia then swing outwards and forwards to contact the stigmas which lie laterally. I have seen a bee which had been visiting the orchid *Barlia robertiana* on the island of Crete so loaded down with fourteen sets of pollinia clamped round its proboscis that it could scarcely fly and was frantically trying to brush them off with its forelegs.

The pollen masses of the Common Twayblade (*Listera ovata*) are very crumbly in texture, and tend to be deposited in a yellow mass on the rostellum. Small insects are attracted by the nectar secreted in a groove along the centre of the labellum, and if they touch the rostellum a small drop of sticky fluid is released explosively, glueing some pollen onto the insect's head and scaring it off to another flower.

Many orchids possess a well-developed rostellum, positioned like a shelf between the base of the pollinia and the stigma, where it acts to prevent self-pollination or autogamy. In some species the rostellum is poorly developed or shrivels up early, even before the flowers are fully open, so that the pollen masses can fall directly on to the stigma. This is the commonest method in the helleborines and is highly efficient, as judged by the number of large, fat seed capsules which are formed.

Self-pollination occurs with considerable frequency in the Bee Orchid (*Ophrys apifera*), despite the fact that the flowers are apparently adapted by mimicry for insect pollination and possess a large projecting rostellum. Close examination will show that the caudicles bearing the pollen masses shrink as the plant matures, pulling the pollinia out of their bursicles so that they swing down under their own weight past the rostellum on to the stigma. For this reason hybrids of the Bee Orchid are extremely rare.

The closely related Early Spider-orchid (*Ophrys sphegodes*) relies on pollination by the Solitary Bee (*Andrena nigroaena*). The orchid operates a sexual swindle, secreting pheromones that attract the male bee, which attempts to mate with the flower – a process called pseudocopulation – and in so doing removes the pollinia. The bee exhibits frantic excitement under the influence of the pheromones. A Swiss botanist visiting Beachy Head with me captured a bee *in flagrante*, and took it back to Switzerland in a little sample tube. Three days later he introduced it to a Swiss Early Spider-orchid, when it promptly repeated the process, its ardour undiminished by the passage of time and a flight by Swiss Air.

The Fly Orchid (*Ophrys insectifera*) is pollinated by pseudocopulating males of the Digger Wasp (*Argogorytes mystaceus*), which emerge before the females, during which time they visit many Fly Orchid flowers. Once the genuine female insects are on the wing they realise the error of their ways and chase the females instead. In the 1970s a botanist, Howard Jones, took some superb colour photographs of the wasp on a Fly Orchid, the earliest photographic record made of pseudocopulation.

It is noteworthy that the sweet scent of the butterfly orchids is mainly produced at night, since they are visited mainly by night-flying moths. The scent of the Early-purple Orchid is quite sweet when the flowers first open, but once they have been pollinated it changes, to smell strongly of tomcat's urine, possibly to deter insects from wasting effort on flowers which no longer require their attentions. The flowers of the Lizard Orchid (*Himantoglossum hircinum*) have a strong smell that reminds most people of goats.

The list of the insect pollinators of British orchids is far from complete and offers a fascinating field for anyone with some expertise in both plants and insects, along with endless patience. It is one thing to observe an insect visiting an orchid, and quite another to be sure that the visit results in active pollination. Ants and other small insects will visit orchids and remove portions of pollinia as nutrient-rich food for their offspring, but this does not necessarily lead to pollination.

Classification

The classification and identification of the orchids of Great Britain provides many problems for the amateur botanist, compounded by their structural complexity and their tendency to produce varieties and made more difficult by the changes of nomenclature which have occurred as our knowledge of them has increased.

Recent work involving investigation of the DNA of plants has meant many suggestions for radical changes in nomenclature. Not all these changes are universally acceptable, and for the moment I have opted to keep the scientific nomenclature I used in A Guide to the Wild Orchids of Great Britain and Ireland (OUP 1989).

The common English names are another source of controversy, in part because of the current desire that all common names should be binomial, leading to the use of hyphenation. Thus *Pseudorchis albida* becomes the Small-white Orchid and *Dactylorhiza fuchsii* becomes the Common Spotted-orchid. It seems that everything must be made to fit into neat little boxes, even if – like the Ugly Sisters in Hans Christian Andersen's story – it involves chopping off the toes to make their feet fit into Cinderella's slipper.

The classification of species serves to help us identify what we are looking at (an activity which is almost an obsession with the human species), but it is well to remember that we are imposing a structure on a creation capable of infinite variety, and that the boundaries of species may well be blurred. The study of taxonomy and the investigation of the fine differences between species is totally fascinating and great fun, provided that we keep a sense of proportion.

Thirty-three species of orchids have been recorded with reasonable certainty in Sussex, and a further three – the Military Orchid (*Orchis militaris*), the Monkey Orchid (*Orchis simia*) and the Late Spider-orchid (*Ophrys fuciflora*) – are reputed to have been seen, on evidence that varies from possible to highly improbable.

The Family Orchidaceae are divided into the Sub-Family Diandrae which possess two stamens and the Monandrae which have only one. All the orchids occurring in Sussex belong to the latter family.

The following chart lists all the thirty-three Sussex species under their tribes, sub-tribes, genera and species, giving their current scientific Latin names and their common English names. The names or initials following the Latin are those of the botanists who first described the species, the names being abbreviated in some cases (*ie*. L. stands for Carl Linnaeus), or placed in parenthesis if the definition has subsequently been changed, (*ie*. (L.) Kuntze where Kuntze's alternative name for the plant has been adopted). Those marked with an asterisk have not recently been recorded in Sussex, and may be extinct in the county.

In the individual species descriptions I have included some of the historical scientific names in square brackets. These are not currently used, but since they may appear in old botanical books, I felt that they could be useful for reference.

DIVISION ACROTONAE

TRIBE Neottiae

Sub-tribe i.Cephalantherinae

1.*Cephalanthera damasonium* (Miller)Druce **White Helleborine**
2.*Cephalanthera longifolia* (L.)Fritsch **Sword-leaved Helleborine**
3.*Cephalanthera rubra* * (L.)Rich. **Red Helleborine**

Sub-tribe ii.Epipactinae

4.*Epipactis palustris* (L.)Crantz **Marsh Helleborine**
5.*Epipactis helleborine* (L.)Crantz **Broad-leaved Helleborine**
6 *Epipactis purpurata* Smith **Violet Helleborine**
7.*Epipactis leptochila* (Godfery)Godfery **Narrow-lipped Helleborine**
8.*Epipactis phyllanthes* G.E.Smith **Pendulous-flowered Helleborine**

Sub-tribe iii.Spiranthinae

9.*Spiranthes spiralis* (L.)Chevallier **Autumn Lady's-tresses**

Sub-tribe iv.Listerinae

10. *Listera ovata* (L.)R.Brown **Common Twayblade**
11.*Listera cordata* * (L.)R.Brown **Lesser Twayblade**
12.*Neottia nidus-avis*(L.)Rich. **Bird's-nest Orchid**

TRIBE Epidendrae

Sub-tribe Liparidinae

13.*Hammarbya paludosa* * (L.)Kuntze **Bog Orchid**

DIVISION BASITONAE

TRIBE Orchideae

Sub-tribe i.Gymnadeniinae

14.*Herminium monorchis*(L.)R.Brown **Musk Orchid**
15.*Coeloglossum viride*(L.)Hartman **Frog Orchid**
16.*Gymnadenia conopsea*(L.)R.Brown **Fragrant Orchid**
17.*Pseudorchis albida* * (L.)A&D.Loeve **Small-white Orchid**
18.*Platanthera chlorantha*(Custer)Reichenbach **Greater Butterfly-orchid**
19.*Platanthera bifolia*(L.)Richard **Lesser Butterfly-orchid**

Sub-tribe ii.Serapiadinae

20.*Ophrys apifera* Hudson **Bee Orchid**
21.*Ophrys sphegodes* Miller **Early Spider-orchid**
22.*Ophrys insectifera* L. **Fly Orchid**
23.*Himantoglossum hircinum* (L.)Sprengel **Lizard Orchid**
24.*Orchis purpurea* * Hudson **Lady Orchid**
25.*Orchis ustulata* L. **Burnt Orchid**
26.*Orchis morio* L. **Green-winged Orchid**
27.*Orchis mascula* (L.)L. **Early-Purple Orchid**
28.*Dactylorhiza fuchsii* (Druce)Soó **Common Spotted-Orchid**
29.*Dactylorhiza maculata* (L.)Soó ssp.*ericetorum* (E.F.Linton)Hunt & Summerhayes **Heath Spotted-Orchid**
30.*Dactylorhiza incarnata* (L.)Soó **Early Marsh-Orchid**
31.*Dactylorhiza praetermissa* (Druce)Soó **Southern Marsh-Orchid**
32.*Aceras anthropophorum* (L.)Aitken.f. **Man Orchid**
33.*Anacamptis pyramidalis* (L.)Richard **Pyramidal Orchid**

* **Not recently recorded in Sussex, and possibly extinct.**

In the following text the characteristics of each genus are described, which can act as a guide in assigning an unknown orchid plant. These notes are not exhaustive, but when taken with the detailed description of each species and accompanying photographs should enable one to identify all the species which occur in Sussex. Technical terms used are explained in the **Glossary**.

TRIBE Neottiae

The stamen is found at the back of the column. This group includes all the helleborines, lady's-tresses and twayblades.

Genus *Cephalanthera*

Shortly rhizomatous plants with leafy stems and lax spikes, with a few large, sub-erect white or pink sessile flowers which never open widely. The lip has a cup-shaped hypochile which clasps the column.

The middle of the lip is constricted, and the distal portion the epichile, bears ridges on its upper surface, and has a recurved tip. There is no spur.

Genus *Epipactis*

Rhizomatous plants with leafy stems bearing sheathing scales at the base. The largest leaves are borne near the middle of the stem. Flowers in a one-sided raceme. The labellum is divided into hypochile and epichile, and bears two bosses at its base. There are no ridges on the epichile and there is no spur.

Genus *Spiranthes*

Small plants with tuberous roots, leafy stems and flowers in a spirally twisted spike. Flowers are tube-shaped, the upper lip formed by the adherent perianth segments, the lower lip formed by the frilled labellum. There is no spur.

Genus *Listera*

Plants with short rhizomes and a pair of opposite leaves some way up the stem. Flowers in a lax raceme with perianth segments similar in length except the labellum, which is forked to midway. There is no spur.

Genus *Neottia*

Plants lack chlorophyll and have a dense, tangled root mass. Flowers brown, in a fairly dense spike. Upper perianth segments form a hood, labellum forked at the tip. There is no spur.

TRIBE Epidendrae

The stamen is borne near the top of the column.

Genus *Hammarbya*

Small green plants, usually growing in *Sphagnum* moss. Pseudobulb at the base of the stem, small concave leaves with tiny green bulbils on their margins. Flowers small and green, with the labellum pointing upwards.

TRIBE Orchideae

The stamen is attached by its base to the front of the column. The viscidia lie on either side of the entrance to the spur, where it is present.

Genus *Herminium*

Small plants with a single tuber and several satellite tubers borne on slender rhizomes. Several narrow base leaves and a single stem leaf. Dense flower spike of tiny yellow-green flowers, the labellum three-lobed. There is no spur.

Genus *Coeloglossum*

Plants with palmate tubers, oval base leaves and narrow stem leaves. Flower spike dense, the outer perianth segments forming a hood above the strap-shaped labellum which has three lobes at the tip. Colour green or brown. There is a short spur.

Genus *Gymnadenia*
Plants with palmate tubers – divided like the fingers of a hand. Stems with long, narrow leaves and a long, densely packed spike of scented flowers. The lateral perianth segments are spreading, the others forming a hood. Labellum three-lobed, spur long and slender. The two pollinia are carried on a single viscidium.

Genus *Pseudorchis*
Tubers entire. Leaves broad oval, with narrower stem leaves. Flower spike rather lax, with small, white, scented flowers. Outer perianth segments are spreading, the others forming a hood. Labellum narrow and strap-shaped, with a long, narrow spur. The two pollinia have separate viscidia.

Genus *Platanthera*
Tubers entire and tapering. Basal leaves broad oval, shiny, the upper stem leaves grading into the bracts. Flower spike lax with white, strongly scented flowers. Lateral perianth segments spreading, the others forming a hood. Labellum long, decurved and strap-shaped, with a long narrow spur. The pollinia have separate viscidia attached to the sides of the spur entrance.

Genus *Ophrys*
The tubers are globular, the leaves elongated, blunt-ended and parallel veined. By the time of flowering the tips of the leaves are frequently withered. The flower spike carries a few large flowers. The perianth segments are spreading, the labellum large and distinctive, convex, furry and dark coloured, with conspicuous markings. There is no spur. The column is prominent and the pollinia are borne on long caudicles.

Genus *Himantoglossum*
The tubers are broad, the leaves numerous and pale green, usually somewhat withered by the time the flowering spike matures. The plant is massive, the flowering spike carrying many strong-smelling flowers. The perianth segments form a compact, rounded helmet. The curious long labellum has two lateral lobes, narrow and crinkled, and a long central lobe, initially coiled up like a watch-spring, unfurling and twisting spirally as the flower opens. There is a short spur.

Genus *Orchis*
The tubers are spherical or ovoid. The unspotted lower leaves form a rosette, while the upper leaves sheath the stem. The bracts are thin and membranous. The perianth segments form a hood. The labellum is divided into three lobes, which may be sub-divided, and bears a spur.

Genus *Dactylorhiza*
The tubers are divided palmately. The basal leaves may be spotted, but do not form a rosette in the mature plant. The bracts are leafy, and the perianth segments are erect or spreading, not in the form of a hood. There is a spur.

Genus *Aceras*
The tubers are ovoid. The lower leaves are long, narrow and unspotted, with stem leaves grading into the bracts. The flowers are greenish yellow or brown tinged, borne in a long narrow spike. The perianth segments form a helmet-shaped hood from which hangs the labellum, having two side lobes and a strongly forked tip, so it is shaped like a little man. There is no spur.

Genus *Anacamptis*
The tubers are ovoid. The leaves are narrow and numerous, the brightly coloured flowers borne in a dense conical spike. The three-lobed labellum has two oblique, erect plates at its base, which serve as guides to the long slender spur.

Hybridisation

The occurrence of hybrids among orchid populations in Britain is not unusual, but does lead to substantial problems in their interpretation. Dr C.A. Stace in Hybridization and the Flora of the British Isles defines a species as 'a unit of practical value, visually recognisable and of evolutionary significance. Morphological and genetical data should be used in its recognition.'

A hybrid can be defined as the offspring between two different taxa, either different species or different genera, the hybrid thus formed being either an interspecific or an intergeneric hybrid. Interspecific hybrids can lead to new fertile species in one step, but usually the influence of hybridisation on evolution is far more subtle. Interspecific hybrids may develop or fail under the influence of natural selection, particularly since characters can appear in the hybrid which are not apparent in either parent.

The first generation (F1) hybrid may itself be diluted by repeated back-crossing with one of the parents, a process called 'introgression'. Fertile hybrids should not be taken as evidence that the two species are closely related. It is not possible to predict the level of fertility of a hybrid from the closeness of the parental relationship. Hybrids between vastly different taxa can be fully fertile, while hybrids between such closely related taxa as Common Spotted-orchid (*Dactylorhiza fuchsii*) and Heath Spotted-orchid (*Dactylorhiza maculata* ssp. *ericetorum*) are highly sterile.

The formation of natural hybrids from potential parents depends upon many factors. Isolation will prevent pollen exchange if the distance is too great, species may not flower at the same time of year, or pollen incompatability may cause the pollen tube to die before the egg is fertilised. Even if fertilisation occurs, it may fail because of early embryonic death. Hybridisation between *Ophrys* species is rare because the insect vector is attracted by pheromones to the one species, and ignores the others even when available.

Hybrid vigour will be evidenced where the chance combination of genetic factors from both parents is favourable. Spectacularly large and floriferous specimens can result. Equally the combination could result in a miserable little hybrid, or even be lethal. It is all chance.

If the F1 generation is self-sterile (F1 x F1 = sterile), then it can only reproduce by back-crossing or introgression, the procedure giving rise to a range of individuals intermediate in characteristics between the F1 and the parent species. Such a range of plants is called a hybrid swarm, and is not uncommon among the *Dactylorhiza*. Environmental circumstances can act upon such populations, eliminating one parent entirely, leaving the swarm and one identifiable progenitor, and making the interpretation very difficult.

● **Cockayne in 1923 established three criteria which should be satisfied before the identity of a hybrid can be assumed: 1. the plant should be morphologically intermediate between the putative parents; 2. it should grow in the field in proximity to both parents; and 3. if it is fertile there should be segregation of types in the F2 and successive generations.**

Summerhayes (1968) described a hybrid between the Fragrant Orchid (*Gymnadenia conopsea*) and the Common Spotted-orchid (*Dactylorhiza fuchsii*). A bursicle is present around the pollinia of *Dactylorhiza* but absent from *Gymnadenia*. In his hybrid he found flowers with bursicles, imperfectly formed bursicles or no bursicles at all, all on the same flower spike. This shows how difficult it is to satisfy Cockayne's Criteria.

Mapping

I well remember an aunt of mine expressing total bemusement that anyone should want to map plants. Yet good distribution maps can tell us such a lot about plants and are invaluable tools in telling us whether certain species are increasing or decreasing, guiding us in making choices for their conservation.

The distribution pattern of any plant will reflect its growth requirements. The Fragrant Orchid (*Gymnadenia conopsea*) grows chiefly on the chalk in Sussex, so that the pattern will follow the outline of the South Downs. The Heath Spotted-orchid (*Dactylorhiza maculata* ssp.*ericetorum*) likes acid soils and heathlands, so shows a preference for Ashdown Forest and the West Sussex heaths.

The mapping system used in this book is recommended for plant recording by the Botanical Society of the British Isles (BSBI). The National Grid used in the Ordnance Survey maps divides Great Britain into 100Km squares, with a reference point south-west of Lands End, from which the grid extends to cover the entire country. The largest squares are 100 x 100Km, sub-divided into 10Km and then into 1Km squares. Within the 1Km square, using the OS 1-50 000 map, it is relatively simple to estimate the position of a site to within 100m, giving a six-figure reference. Each 100Km square is designated by two letters. SU covers most of West Sussex and TQ covers part of West and nearly all of East Sussex, with the Selsey peninsula in SZ and Beachy Head in TV.

The recent introduction of global positioning satellites (GPS) makes it possible to fix a position within 10m, enabling the operator to make an exact record even in the depths of an otherwise featureless wood. Just imagine how useful it would be to know precisely where the likes of Borrer, Hilton or Guermonprez found an orchid all those years ago: not just 'Downs above Lewes 1853', but a precise spot!

The distribution maps in this book show the main 10 x 10Km squares sub-divided into squares of 2 x 2Km. A solid circle indicates that the orchid has recently been found in that area in at least one site. An empty square indicates that it has never grown there, while a hollow circle indicates that it did so previously but has now gone. You can see at a glance how some species have declined or even disappeared from Sussex since the start of recording in the 18th century.

How to read an Ordnance Survey map

Ditchling Beacon TQ 532 113

53(2) The first three numbers lead you across the map left to right. Find 53 at the bottom and then imagine the following square divided into tenths: run your finger two-tenths towards 54

11(3) Now, similarly read up to 11 and continue three-tenths towards 12.

The Species

1 White Helleborine
2 Sword-leaved Helleborine
3 Red Helleborine*
4 Marsh Helleborine
5 Broad-leaved Helleborine
6 Violet Helleborine
7 Slender-lipped Helleborine
8 Pendulous-flowered Helleborine
9 Autumn Lady's-tresses
10 Common Twayblade
11 Lesser Twayblade*
12 Bird's-nest Orchid
13 Bog Orchid*
14 Musk Orchid
15 Frog Orchid
16 Fragrant Orchid
17 Small-white Orchid*
18 Greater Butterfly-orchid
19 Lesser Butterfly-orchid
20 Bee Orchid
21 Early Spider-orchid
22 Fly Orchid
23 Lizard Orchid
24 Lady Orchid*
25 Burnt Orchid
26 Green-winged Orchid
27 Early-purple Orchid
28 Common Spotted-orchid
29 Heath Spotted-orchid
30 Early Marsh-orchid
31 Southern Marsh-orchid
32 Man Orchid
33 Pyramidal Orchid

** Not recently recorded in Sussex and may be extinct in the county*

1 WHITE HELLEBORINE

Cephalanthera damasonium (Miller) Druce
[*Cephalanthera latifolia* Janchen]

The first record for White Helleborine in Sussex is from a specimen collected by a Mr Watson, possibly the father of Rev H.C. Watson, in 1786 near Goodwood, the herbarium sheet residing at Kew. The next historical record is also from Goodwood, by W.W. Newbould in 1843.

White Helleborine is the commonest member of the genus and can often be found in considerable numbers in mature beech woods. It is a robust and handsome plant 15 – 60cm in height, with a deep-growing, fibrous root mass.

The leaves are oval and strongly ribbed, in two rows up the stem, merging into the leaf-like bracts which are longer than the ovary.

The flowering spike carries up to sixteen ivory white flowers, which lie vertically, close to the stem. The perianth segments do not open widely, so that the flower appears never to be fully open. The labellum consists of a basal hypochile, yellow within, and a heart-shaped epichile which has five darker yellow ridges on the upper surface. The outer ridges are not always obvious.

The ovary is deeply grooved, broader near the tip and untwisted, which differentiates it from the twisted ovary of the closely related Sword-leaved helleborine (*Cephalanthera longifolia*).

There is no rostellum and many flowers are efficiently self-pollinated, although pollination is also carried out by the female solitary bee *Andrena florea*. Mature plants develop more than eight years after the setting of seed, and even then they may not flower for several more years. The flowering season is from early May until the end of June.

White Helleborine is primarily a plant of chalk soils, particularly of mature beech woods, although it can also occasionally be found on open downland. The distribution pattern follows the line of the South Downs, with a few scattered records from mid and east Sussex, where it occurs on calcareous Purbeck beds at Darwell Wood.

There is good evidence that it is declining throughout the county, being lost from a number of sites and much reduced in numbers elsewhere.

Rev F.H. Arnold (1887) recorded it from St.Leonard's Forest and from Newick, while T. Hilton,

Mr Standen and F.C.S. Roper all found it around Brighton in areas which are now completely built over. It has, however, recently been found at Withdean.

More encouraging is the situation in Friston Forest, which is slowly developing into a very fine beech forest. There White Helleborine is increasing in numbers, but more importantly it is appearing in new sites every year.

It is a relatively constant species, although flowers with double tips or double columns can occur. C.B. Tahourdin recorded an unusual plant with white stem and leaves, a form which has been known on the Continent from Saarland. Dr N. Sturt has recorded this form more recently on Duncton Hill.

The hybrid with Sword-leaved Helleborine *Cephalanthera damasonium* x *C.longifolia* (*Cephalanthera* x *schulzei* Camus, Berg & Camus) has been recorded several times in Sussex. It was first found in Great Britain in 1974, when John Lansley and I found it in Hampshire. Brianne Reeve photographed a plant which closely resembled the hybrid in a wood near Chichester in 1995, but it has not since reappeared.

I found the hybrid in 1996 near Arundel, where it flowered again in 2000. The hybrid has leaves which are broad and ridged, the flowers pure white, long stalked but carried close to the stem. The labellum has three ridges on the upper surface of the epichile, and the ovary is intermediate in thickness, but twisted through 180°. In the second Sussex site there is now evidence of introgression with *Cephalanthera damasonium*, producing flowers which closely resemble that parent but have a slightly twisted ovary.

White Helleborine

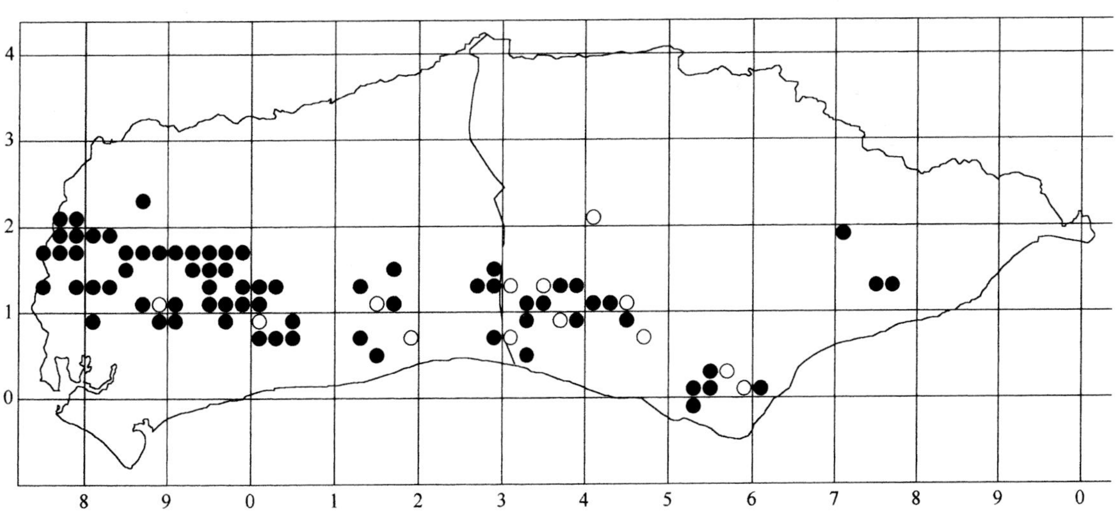

2 SWORD-LEAVED HELLEBORINE

Cephalanthera longifolia (L.) Fritsch

Pure white flowers and long elegant leaves make the Sword-leaved Helleborine a far more elegant plant than White Helleborine.

The first record we have of the species in Sussex is for a plant collected in 1826 by Rev R.F. Bree from a beechwood in Goodwood Park. It was collected there in the following year 1827 by H.C. Watson, and is in his herbarium at Kew. It continued to flourish there, with a further collection made by W.W. Newbould in 1843, and was last recorded near the grandstand in 1970 by Maj W.W. Phillips.

It was known from Stanmer Park, Brighton in 1891, where both T. Hilton and H.L.F. Guermonprez collected it, not far from a site where a student from Sussex University found it in 1979. This was confirmed in 1982 by David Streeter, but a search in 1999 could not relocate it, and the copse was densely overgrown.

It lasted for many years in a copse by a chalkpit near Lavant. Pressed specimens collected by Dr F.V. Paxton in 1875 can be seen in F.C.S. Roper's herbarium, and further specimens collected by D. Paxton in 1880 are in Rev F.H. Arnold's herbarium. (Dr Paxton, who lived in the Pallants in Chichester and was an active member of the Chichester and West Sussex Natural History and Microscopical Society, had a penchant for introducing plants to the wild.) Guermonprez painted it there in 1915, when R.J. Burden also recorded it, and it was last seen and photographed in 1966 by Peter Newey.

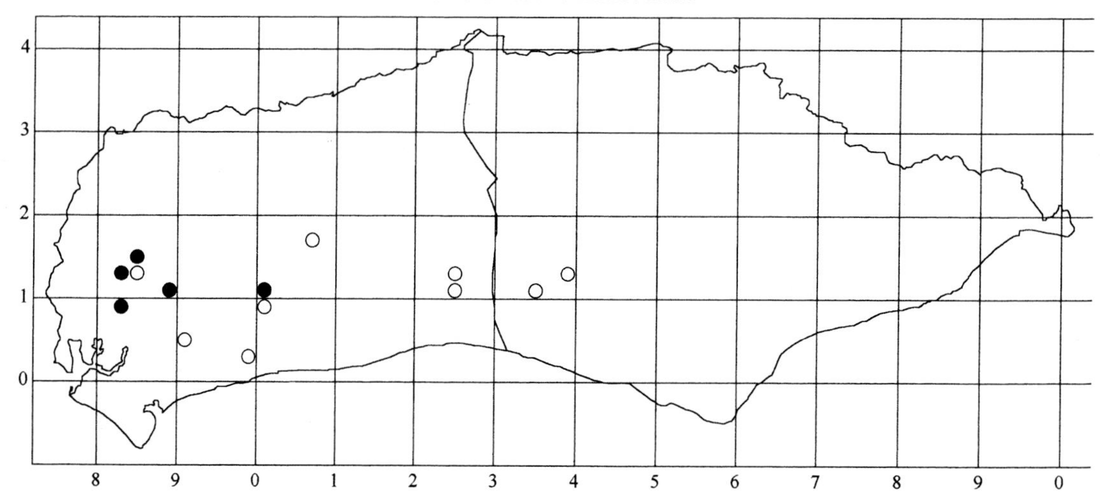

There are various vague references to it near Lewes, collected in 1879 and 1897 by J.H.A. Jenner (Roper's herbarium), and in June 1900 by T. Hilton from an unnamed site. Guermonprez found it near Offham in 1900, where it was later recorded by Lady Davey in 1923 and H. Salt in 1928, when there were twenty flowering spikes. Since then it has disappeared, but current forestry work gives rise to hopes that it could reappear.

H.G. Billingshurst and C.E. Salmon found it near Arundel in 1905 in a wood where Tahourdin records it in 1927. It is still there and appears secure. It is also still present in a wood near Kingley Vale, where Francis Rose saw it in 1958, although in much smaller numbers than the seventy plants recorded there in 1967 by Richard Williamson.

There is ample evidence that everywhere it is decreasing in numbers and vanishing from known sites. There are old records for sites between Ardingly and Cuckfield (possibly erroneous), Dale Down near Arundel and between Fulking and Holmbush, but none have been seen there for many years.

Sword-leaved Helleborine can reach 160cm in height, but most of the plants I have seen recently do not exceed 25cm. The numerous leaves are long, narrow and pointed, grading into bracts which are shorter than the ovary.

Even at a distance among White Helleborines the pure white flowers stand out. The flower spike is lax and the flowers are borne almost horizontally, well away from the stem. The perianth segments are long, pointed and spreading, exposing the pointed labellum. The epichile bears three ridges on its upper surface, and these are usually orange in colour rather than yellow. The flowers are sensitive to cold and wet, and are often defaced with brown spots. The ovary is slim, cylindrical in outline, and twisted in a spiral through 180°.

Self-pollination is prevented by the position of the rostellum, pollination being carried out by female solitary bees *Lasioglossum smeathmannellum*. The Hampshire Wildlife Trust have recorded *Lasioglossum fulvicornis* as a pollinator. Few ripe seed capsules are produced, unlike the plentiful setting of the White Helleborine.

Sword-leaved Helleborine is very uncommon and declining, although widely distributed in Great Britain. It is one of the species currently under investigation by Plant Life's 'Back from the Brink' project. Most of the Sussex sites are in beech woods on chalk, much more open and well lit than those favoured by White Helleborine. It was noticeable in one site that the greatest concentration of flowers followed what had obviously been an old vehicle track. The increased illumination does however encourage brambles and scrub, which can swamp the plants.

Sword-leaved Helleborine flowers throughout May, about two weeks earlier than White Helleborine. Variation is very rare, and the hybrid *Cephalanthera* x *schulzei* has been described under White Helleborine.

3 RED HELLEBORINE

Cephalanthera rubra (L.) Richard

The Red Helleborine is probably one of the most striking orchids which occur in Great Britain, combining a graceful shape with flowers of a luminous pink. It has long been known from Gloucestershire, was discovered in the Chilterns in 1955 and in Hampshire in 1986. At present the status of Red Helleborine in Sussex must necessarily be that of a 'factoid', but the history behind this state is fascinating and proof of its existence remains a botanical Holy Grail.

The first reference I can discover is for a plant or plants which grew on the bank alongside a garden just west of Houghton in 1910. There is no information to indicate whether they were considered at the time to be wild or introduced, and Wolley-Dod makes no reference to them in his Flora of 1937. In 1921 several specimens were seen in the hands of a woodcutter near Poling, and recognised by H.M. Edelsten who knew the plant well in Gloucestershire.

In 1991 photographs taken by an entomologist in a wood near Arundel clearly show *Cephalanthera rubra*, although the background to the photographs gives no clear indication of the exact site. The area where they were reported has been repeatedly searched to no avail.

It is well documented that Red Helleborine can remain in a vegetative state for many years, and it would be sheer luck to spot and identify the foliage among the other woodland plants. The flowering spike is not tall, 20-60cm, most plants in this country being rather small. The root system is composed of thin horizontal roots from which buds arise forming new aerial stems. The leaves are short and dark, and the slender bracts exceed the ovaries.

Continental plants have been recorded with fifteen flowers, but most British plants carry three to five, the large unopened buds having a marked resemblance to freesias. The perianth segments are long, pointed and pink. The pointed labellum is also pink with a pale yellowish centre, and there are five to seven orange ridges on the epichile. The ovary is narrow, cylindrical and spirally twisted. All the floral parts are covered in glandular hairs, especially the posterior surfaces of the outer perianth segments.

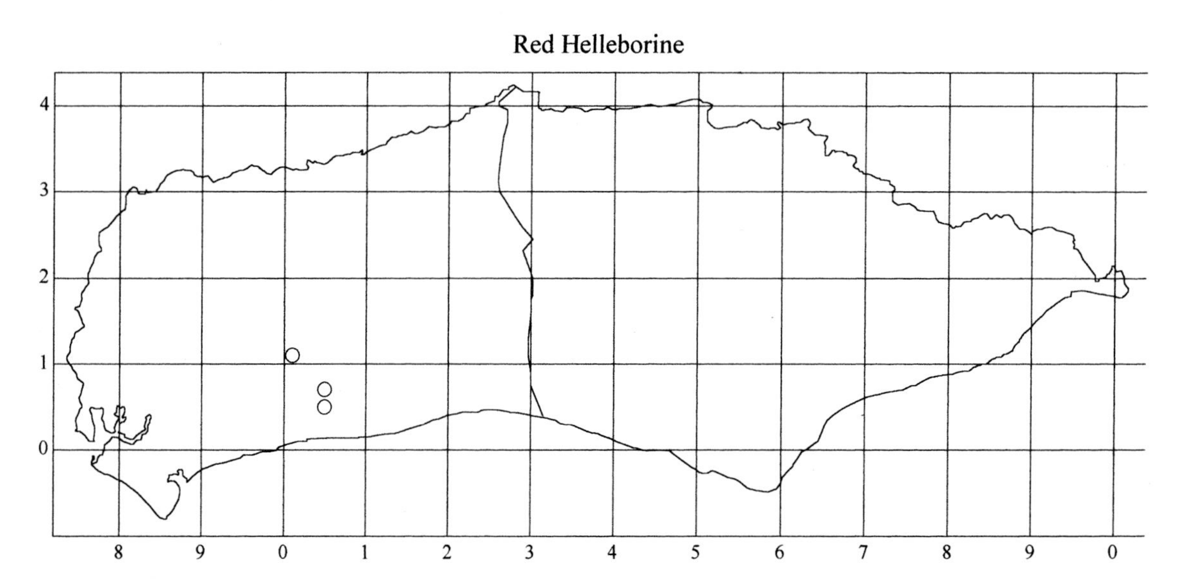

Pollination has been recorded by the male Mason Bee (*Osmia caerulescens*) and by a small solitary bee, possibly *Chelostoma fuliginosa*. I have seen flowers visited by a number of small hoverflies, and once by a Small Skipper (*Thymelicus sylvestris*).

Research by Dr L. Anders Nilsson on the island of Gotland in the Baltic has shown that no nectar is produced, but the colour is perceived by the bees to be the same as that of the nectar producing campanulas. The pink colour we see is beyond the range of the bee's visual system and chemical analysis of the fragrance shows it to be quite different to that of the campanula. So it is the colour which is the attractant, and which creates the deceit.

The Red Helleborine is a plant of beech woods on chalk or limestone, and its ability to flower is highly dependant upon the amount of light where it grows. For this reason there is hope that future forest clearance may create the circumstances for it to appear for sure in Sussex. It is heartening to record that its rediscovery in Hampshire in 1986, after an absence of very many years, was in a new site.

It flowers from late June to the end of July.

4 MARSH HELLEBORINE

Epipactis palustris (L.) Crantz

This very beautiful orchid has suffered a catastrophic decline throughout Sussex, as a glance at the distribution map will clearly show. The first record is at Funtington in West Sussex in 1834, from where it had gone in Arnold's time in 1887. He records it as abundant at Aldermere near Westbourne, and S. Baker collected it from the Hunston/Runcton area in 1879 and 1883. Both these sites still held plants in 1921, and a fine painting of the Aldermere plants done by H.L.F. Guermonprez in July of that year is in the City Museum at Portsmouth.

Marsh Helleborine was widely distributed throughout East and West Sussex, with a number of colonies in wet marshes or wet fields below the north face of the Downs. Thomas Hilton knew it at Perching Sands in 1896, where it had already disappeared by 1910, and it was found by C.E. Salmon at Coxbrooks south of High Hurstwood near Uckfield, at Argos Hill and near Eridge. One specimen in C.S. Roper's herbarium was collected on the bank of the London-Brighton railway line west of Bexhill in 1895. It was known for many years in a damp meadow at Ditchling – one of F.F. Woods' sites in 1926 – and it was still there in July 1944, but all these sites have been drained and improved, and the plant has now vanished.

Maude Robinson, who lived at Saddlescombe in the late 1800s, used to ride out every year to see Marsh Helleborine. She would stable her horse at a nearby farm, tuck up the skirts of her riding habit – and as she said in 1945, 'habits had skirts half a century ago!' – and forage about until she found it. She informed a famous local botanist, a Fellow of the Linnaean Society, who was delighted. She later met him coming out of the meadow with the plant in one hand and a trowel in the other. It was never seen there again.

Marsh Helleborine is not a tall plant, the stem 20-60cm arising from a system of fibrous, creeping rhizomes. The leaves are numerous, pointed and sharply folded. There are three to five prominent veins in the leaves, and the leaf bases are often violet-tinged.

The flowering spike is well spaced, with up to twenty large flowers, the lower bracts exceeding and the upper bracts shorter than the pear-shaped, untwisted ovaries.

The outer perianth segments are pointed and purplish brown, the inner ones white with pinkish streaks at the base. The labellum is white, with a hinge joining the hypochile and epichile. The hypochile is marked with parallel reddish veins, the epichile is large and rounded, with a frilly edge and an erect, crinkly yellow plate across the base. The whole effect is charming and resembles a miniature *Cymbidium*, making this species the closest we have in Britain to the popular concept of what an orchid should look like.

The yellow plate on the epichile secretes nectar and attracts a variety of insects. Darwin suggested that the hinged labellum catapulted the visiting insect onto the pollinia, but L.A. Nilsson, working on the Baltic island of Öland, found that male solitary wasps of the genus *Eumenes* tended to lose their balance when they landed on the epichile, and their heads contacted the viscidia. This glued pollen on to them.

Studies in Holland have shown that Honey Bees (*Apis mellifica*) caused 25% of insect pollination when they collected the pollinia for larval food, but ants were the most frequent cause (50%). They disrupted the pollen masses, which then fell onto the stigma, so causing self-pollination. Other insect pollinators include a small black wasp *Psen palustris* and a cantharid beetle, the Bloodsucker (*Rhagonychus fulva*), but vegetative reproduction by shoots developed from the rhizomes appears to be the main method of multiplication.

Marsh Helleborine is a plant of wetmarsh, fens and old damp meadows. It flowers from early July to early September. It still hangs on in two sites in West Sussex, and at a Sussex Wildlife Trust marsh reserve at Balcombe, but numbers there are seriously reduced from the 300 I saw flowering there in 1967. The story in East Sussex is more encouraging, with four colonies in the Rye area.

Dwarf forms and a pale yellow form, var. *ochroleuca*, are known elsewhere in Britain, but do not occur in Sussex. There are no known hybrids.

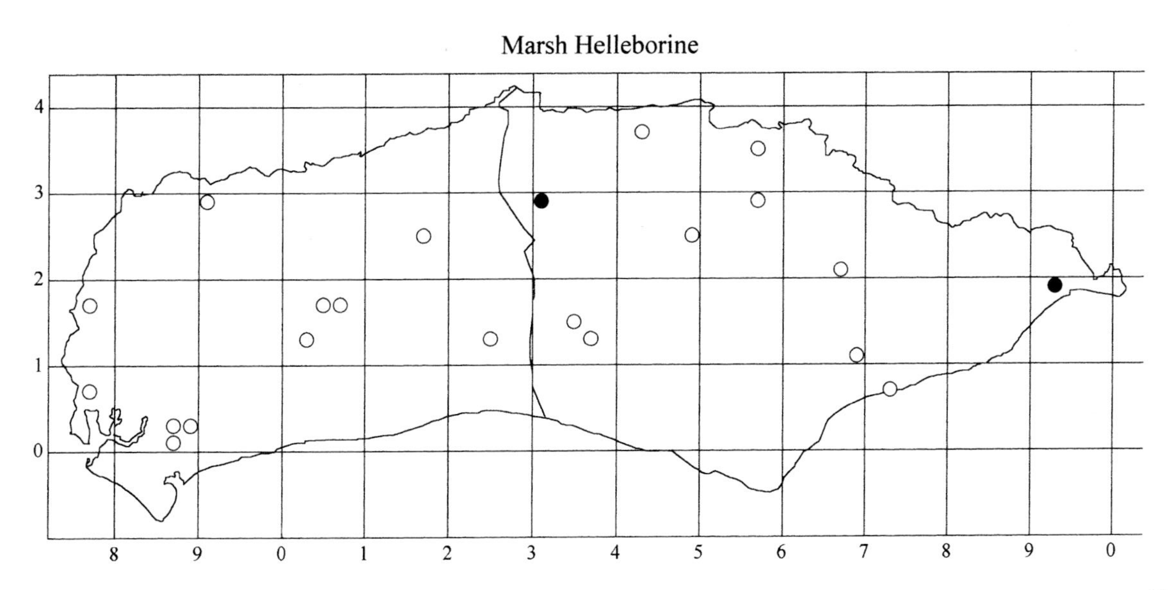

5 BROAD-LEAVED HELLEBORINE

Epipactis helleborine (L.) Crantz
[*Epipactis latifolia* (L.) Allioni]

The very first mention of Broad-leaved Helleborine was from a site near Hastings in 1714 (Wolley-Dod), and next from High Rocks and Harrison's Rocks near Tunbridge Wells in 1816. Arnold (1887) lists a number of locations throughout Sussex from Harting in the west to Guestling in the east, while Wolley-Dod contents himself in noting that it was known in 1937 from at least eighty sites scattered across the county.

There is a fine painting by H.L.F. Guermonprez of a plant from Goodwood Park in July 1893, which is in the Portsmouth Museum.

Broad-leaved Helleborine is robust and tall, frequently exceeding 90cm, with thick clustered roots from which multiple stems can arise. It never forms quite such showy clumps as does the Violet Helleborine (*Epipactis purpurata*).

The leaves are broad oval, dark green and strongly ribbed, arranged spirally up the lower part of the stem. The lower bracts are the same length as the flowers, while the upper bracts are shorter. The whole flower spike can carry up to a hundred flowers in well-lit, favoured localities, and the arrangement of the flowers tends to be one-sided.

The flower is cup-shaped, with greenish outer perianth segments which are broad and blunt, and pinkish upper perianth segments which are smaller. The labellum is divided into a cup-shaped hypochile, dark reddish-brown within and full of sticky nectar. The epichile is pinkish, with a reflexed tip and carries two rough, warty bosses at its base. These serve to differentiate it from the Violet Helleborine, where the bosses are smooth. The rostellum is large and white, and the ovary is smooth and hairless.

There is great variation in the size of plants and the colour of the flowers. Plants growing in deep shade tend to be pale green and etiolated, while those in full sun are robust and may have flowers which are deeply flushed with red. There is great temptation when finding these extremes to think that the plant is one of the rare helleborines, and it is well to remember the maxim that 'common things are common and rare things are rare'. When in doubt, seek expert advice.

The chief insect pollinator appears to be the male Common Wasp *Vespula germanica*.

Plants take about eight years to mature from seed.

Broad-leaved Helleborine flowers from early July to early September. It is mainly a plant of calcareous or sandy woodland, especially under beech, and it enjoys good illumination. It is particularly to be looked for on the verges of paths and roads, especially on rather bare banks under overhanging trees. It is not uncommon in gardens and in urban areas. It is widely distributed throughout Sussex, occurring in 193 tetrads, and is without doubt our most abundant helleborine.

The hybrid *Epipactis helleborine* x *E.purpurata* was described by J.T.H. Knight in 1959, growing near Horsham.

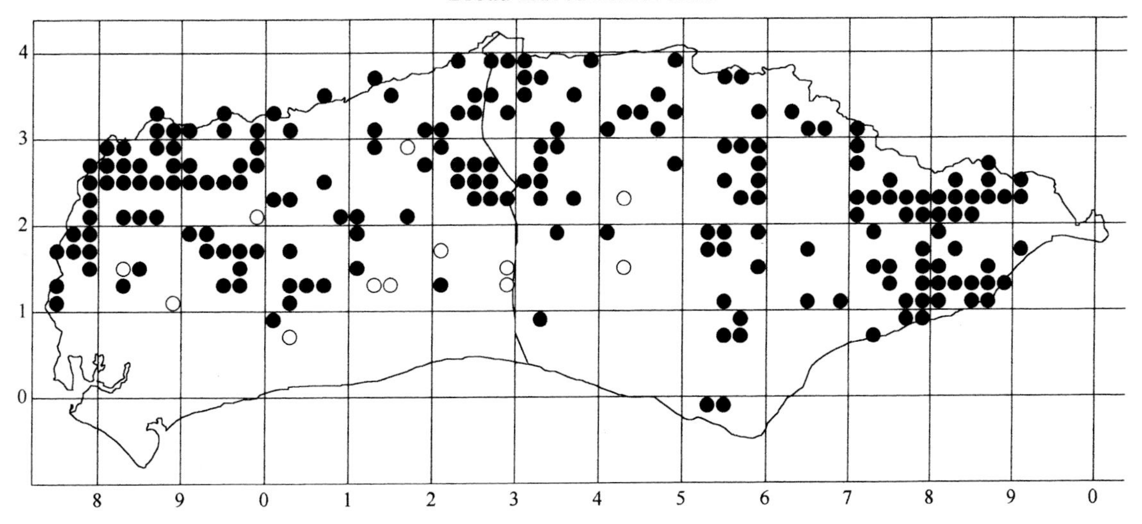

6 VIOLET HELLEBORINE

Epipactis purpurata Smith
[*Epipactis sessilifolia* Peterman; *Epipactis violacea* (Dur.Duq.) Bor.]

A herbarium sheet of a specimen collected in 1885 by a clerical colleague, Rev Parsons, at Stanstead Woods is in Rev F.H. Arnold's herbarium and was claimed by him as the first county record. H.L.F. Guermonprez painted a plant from the same location in 1917. Subsequently I have found some much older records, and the first appears to be that of a plant collected at Crawley in 1834 by C.C. Babington, a friend of William Borrer, with whom he often went out botanising. Arthur Hoare tells me that the plants are still there 161 years later.

There is a herbarium sheet by H.C. Watson at Kew, for Violet Helleborine found at Brook Hill, near Cowfold, in 1856. A finely executed drawing by Borrer is also in the herbarium at Kew, made of a plant he collected at Phillis Wood near Treyford: he had made a number of detailed sketches of the floral structure.

The Violet Helleborine is more elegant than the Broad-leaved Hellobrine, and to my eyes has a slightly sinister appearance, with darker, narrow-leaved foliage. The stems and leaf bases are often suffused with violet. It is less robust but often grows in clumps from the cluster of deep-rooting rhizomes.

The flower spike is distinctly one-sided, and the long narrow bracts give it a rather leafy appearance. The outer perianth segments are green, pointed and spreading, and the upper inner

segments are pale. The labellum is similar in shape to that of the Broad-leaved Helleborine, the hypochile lining pale brown, and the epichile pale pink in colour. However, the two bosses at the base of the epichile are pink and smooth, a clear differentiating character.

Pollination is effected by the male Cuckoo Wasp *Vespula austraica*.

Violet Helleborine flowers about two weeks later than the Broad-leaved Helleborine, in August and September, and tolerates much darker conditions. It is less widespread in Britain, confined mainly to the south-east and south. It is well distributed in East and West Sussex on chalky soils, clay with flints and on the greensand, often growing on roadsides and the edges of paths. It is a tough plant,and I have seen flowering plants pushing up through newly-laid tarmac and between the concrete supports of a fence. The best colonies are to be found in the north and north-west of Sussex in wooded areas bordering Kent and Surrey.

The achlorophyllous form: glowing in the woodland gloom.

There is a curious and very attractive form of the Violet Helleborine which is achlorophyllous – devoid of the green pigment chlorophyll. The stems and leaves are pale pinkish mauve and the flowers almost white, so that the plants appear to glow in the woodland gloom. It has been found near Gravetye, East Grinstead, by Arthur Hoare in 1980, and near Arundel by several observers over the last ten years. Since the plants are flourishing despite their inability to photosynthesise, they must depend upon their mycorrhizal fungus entirely for their nutrition.

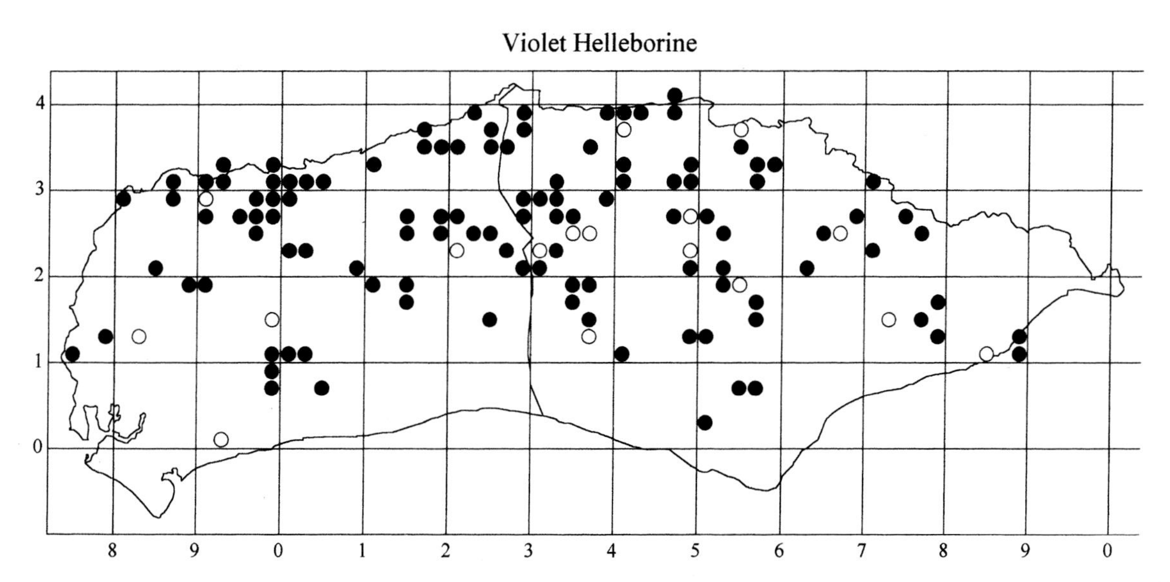

7 SLENDER-LIPPED HELLEBORINE

Epipactis leptochila (Godfery) Godfery
[Inc. *Epipactis cleistogama* C.Thomas]

The Slender-lipped Helleborine was first described by M.J. Godfery as a separate species in 1919 in the Journal of Botany. Although at that time it was thought to be restricted to Great Britain, it has subsequently been recorded in Germany, Denmark, Forêt d'Eu (Normandy) in France and the Valais in Switzerland. In Britain it occurs from Kent westwards to Dorset, but is most frequent in the Chilterns and Cotswolds.

It has a chequered career as a Sussex orchid species, having been found and then lost, misidentified and argued over repeatedly. There is currently doubt that it exists as a proper species. I have visited a wood in South Tyne where typical *Epipactis leptochila* grows at one end of the wood, while the plants at the other end are classical *Epipactis dunensis* (Dune Helleborine). In the area between them, the plants were a glorious muddle of characters. It could well be that the two helleborines are geographical races of the one species, widely separated by time and by environmental circumstances, except where they overlap in the South Tyne valley. All the plants recorded in southern England separate clearly into the taxon recognised as *Epipactis leptochila*.

The first record appears to be that of a specimen found in 1839 in Phillis Wood near Treyford. It was next found in 1852 three miles away at West Dean, where it was collected for William Borrer by Rev W. Wallinger. It was this herbarium sheet which provided the anecdote in **Sussex Botanologia**, being labelled by Borrer as *Epipactis latifolia* – the name then in current use – and then annotated by C.B. Tahourdin and V.S. Summerhayes as *Epipactis leptochila*, incurring the wrath of Dr D.P. Young, who decided it was what we now call the Pendulous-flowered Helleborine (*E. phyllanthes*). I have examined it and find myself in agreement with Tahourdin and Summerhayes.

It was thought to be extinct or misidentified at the site until Miss Dallas Fawdry of Southsea rediscovered it in 1962, but it appears to have died out again, having been last recorded in 1969.

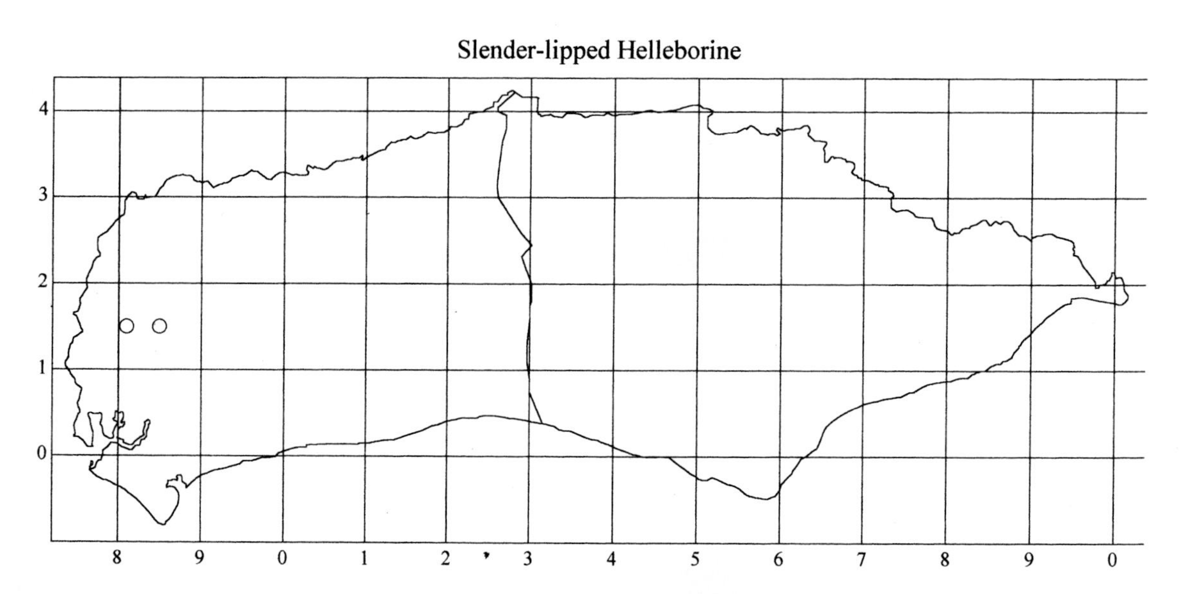

It was recorded for Saxonbury Woods near Tunbridge Wells in 1933 by W.H. Pearsall and A.H. Wolley-Dod, but when a floret from the dried specimen was soaked off and examined by Dr D.P. Young it proved to be the Violet Helleborine (*Epipactis purpurata*). There is a further herbarium sheet in the Natural History Museum collected by C.B. Tahourdin in July 1932, which is certainly *E. leptochila* and definitely from Sussex, but the label had fallen off and been replaced, so that the site – Henfield Common – may not be correct.

Slender-lipped Helleborine is similar in height to Broad-leaved Helleborine (15-60cm), often growing in clumps with up to six flowering stems, with floppy, greenish-yellow, broad leaves in two distinct ranks. The flower spike is lax, with rather large, pendulous flowers set all round the stem.

The perianth segments are very long, pointed and spreading, and all parts except the labellum are plain pale green. The labellum is distinctive. The hypochile is pale brown inside, while the epichile is very long and sharply pointed, the tip not reflexing. The notch at the base of the epichile is deep, giving a strongly 'décolleté neck-line', and the two bosses on either side are small and poorly defined.

There is no rostellum, and the anthers are carried on a stalk in such a manner that, when viewed sideways, there is a distinct hole visible between them and the column. Since there is no rostellum, it has always been assumed that the flowers are autogamous – self-pollinating – as there is no obstruction to pollen falling straight onto the stigma. Some authorities also claim that they are cleistogamous – pollination occurring before the flowers open – but Dr A.J. Richards in Northumberland has observed the German Wasp (*Vespula germanica*) carrying away parts of the pollinia.

The Slender-lipped Helleborine is a strong calcicole and usually occurs in beech or hornbeam woods on chalk, often tolerating deep shade. It flowers earlier than the preceeding two species, from early June to the end of July.

It has never been found in East Sussex, but current searches in the west of the county may lead to its rediscovery.

8 PENDULOUS-FLOWERED HELLEBORINE

Epipactis phyllanthes G.E. Smith
[Includes *Epipactis vectensis* (T. & T.A. Stephenson) Brooke & Rose
E. pendula (C. Thomas)
E. cambrensis (C. Thomas)
E. phyllanthes ssp. *degenera* D.P. Young]

Pendulous-flowered Helleborine was first described by G.E. Smith in 1852 in an article in the Gardener's Chronicle. The specific name has been said to derive from Phillis Wood near Treyford in West Sussex, where it was originally described, but the word *phyllanthes* is literally a Greek compound meaning 'leaf-like flower'. This is more likely in view of the green flowers, although an unidentifiable plant Phyllanthes is mentioned by both the ancient writers Theophrastus and Pliny.

It is widely distributed in England and Wales, where I have seen it as a woodland and shaded-verge plant in Kent, Sussex and in Northumberland, and growing in dune slacks in North Wales at Morfa Dyffryn and in South Wales at Kenfig.

It is a highly variable plant, and has appeared under many names as can be seen by the list above, but I am in full agreement with Dr D.P. Young's paper of 1952 which groups them all as one good species.

Rev G.E. Smith first found Pendulous-flowered Helleborine in 1838 on the downs near Treyford. Preserved material, which was lodged in Druce's collection at Oxford, was examined by Dr Young in 1950, and there is no doubt of its identity. Apart from the disputed material in H.C. Watson's herbarium from 1852, the next collection appears to be that of August 1876,made by W.M. Rogers for William Borrer at 'Stapleford plantation', a site that I have been unable to pinpoint.

In 1959 Dr Young found a thriving colony at Arundel, which was badly damaged later by thoughtless landscaping but has luckily survived, although in reduced numbers. In 1960 a colony was found at West Chiltington Common by Miss D. Long. When the site was visited in 1962 by Dr J.T.H. Knight, he found many plants scythed off by county council road maintenance staff, and I have his letter to V.S. Summerhayes asking his support in lobbying the council to protect the plants. Another site was found nearby at Thakeham in 1962, where in 1999 I found thirty-two flowering spikes, and evidence that it was spreading.

Maj W.W.A. Phillips found Pendulous-flowered Helleborine under beech trees near Goodwood in 1963, and more recently in 1998 a new colony near Arundel was discovered by Suzanne Perry and Bruce Middleton.

Pendulous-flowed Helleborine is rather a small and often delicate looking plant, 10-40cm high, and rarely grows in clumps. The lower stem leaves are stiff and rounded, with up to sixteen leaves borne up the stem in two ranks. Most plants have only three or four leaves. Up to twenty flowers are carried in a fairly dense drooping spike. The large, pear-shaped ovaries are strongly ribbed, with the flowers seeming disproportionately small. The outer perianth segments are green and pointed, much longer than the small upper inner segments, and the labellum is equally small and greenish, with a reflexed tip. The division between the hypochile and the epichile is not well marked, and in some flowers the hypochile is reduced to a shallow depression.

In many of the woodland plants the flowers scarcely open and are always autogamous, in some cases also cleistogamous – fertilisation occurring in the unopened flower. Seed is set effectively and most plants carry plenty of ripe seed capsules.

Pendulous-flowered Helleborine will grow happily in dense shade, often on bare or sparsely covered ground, but it is quite capable of pushing up through a carpet of ivy. It flowers from late June throughout July, and it is usually at its best in the middle of that month.

Although it appears to have its major centre of distribution in the west of Sussex, it should be looked for in any suitable habitat, so often on road verges, and could prove to be more widely distributed. The only source of confusion could be with dwarfed, poorly nourished specimens of Broad-leaved Helleborine (*Epipactis helleborine*).

No hybrids are known.

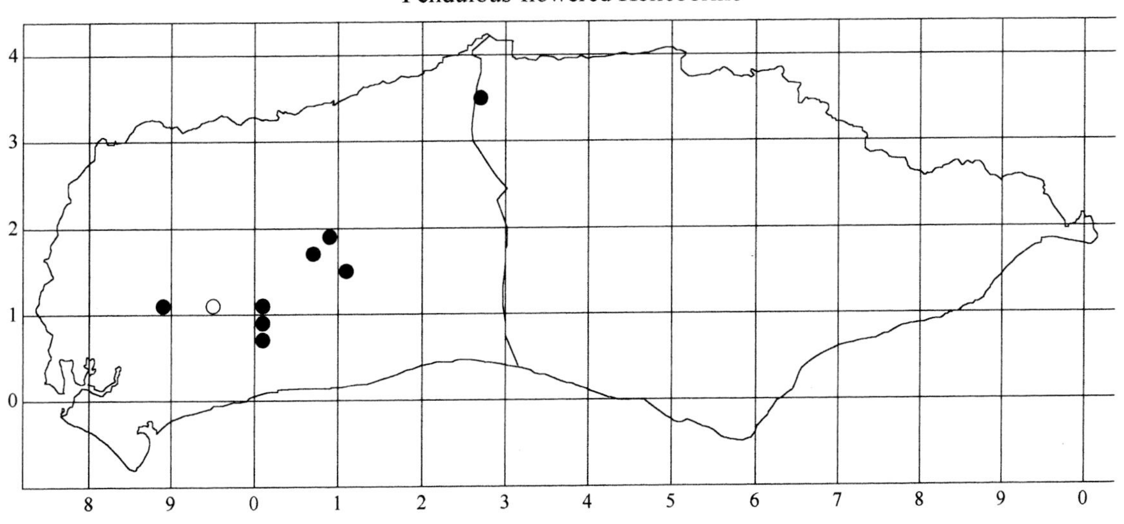

9 AUTUMN LADY'S-TRESSES

Spiranthes spiralis (L.)Chevallier
[*Spiranthes autumnalis* Richard]

Despite its apparent ability to appear by the thousand on lawns and tennis courts and then vanish for years on end, there is no mistaking the diminutive, tightly wound spiral of white flowers. Autumn Lady's-tresses was first recorded from Shoreham in Sussex, where Trevelyan collected it for William Borrer in 1853.

There are numerous herbarium collections from the late 19th century, from Withyham in 1871 by Deakin, from the 'Danish camp' on Roche's Hill near Chichester in 1872 by Rev F.H. Arnold, from Eastbourne in H.L. Green's herbarium at Bexhill in 1872, Ratton in 1874 and Bexhill in 1878 (both by F.C.S.Roper), and many others.

Autumn Lady's-tresses usually has two tubers current at any one time, one rather shrivelled which has supplied the growing flower spike, and a fat white tuber which will supply next season's flower. There is a flat rosette of four or

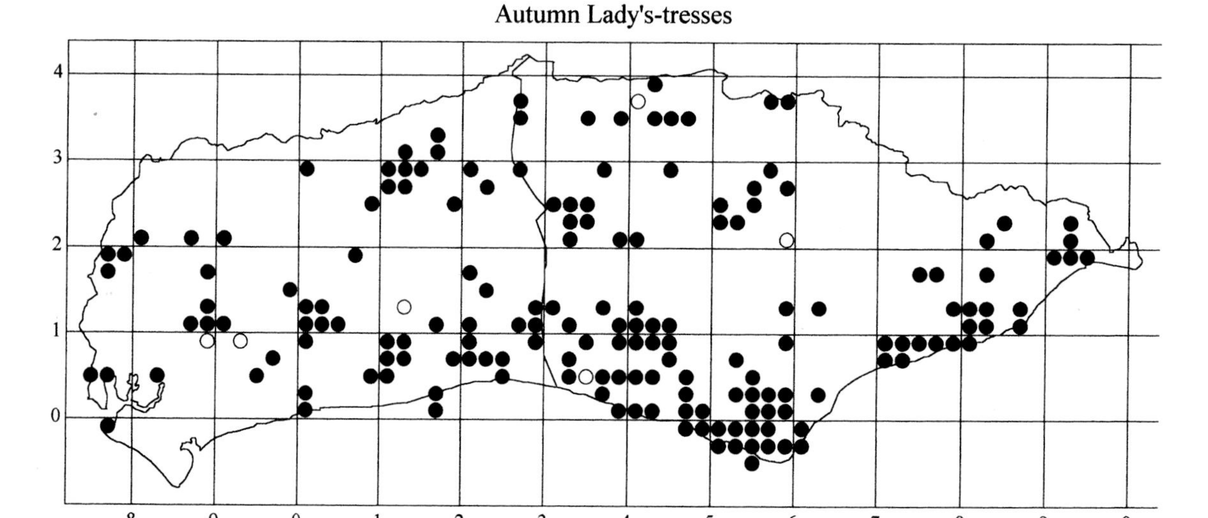

five bluish-green leaves which persist over winter and then wither. The flower spike emerges from the centre of the withered leaves, by which time the new rosette has formed, so that the flower spike and leaves appear to be unconnected. The flat rosette escapes damage from most grazing animals and lawn mowers, but unfortunately rabbits have a great liking for the flower spikes.

The flowering stem, 5-15cm tall, bears up to twenty small, trumpet-shaped white flowers, arranged in a tight spiral. I have to admit that, until I was asked at a lecture, I had never thought whether the twist was clockwise or anti-clockwise. This elicited a panic visit to a large colony which, luckily, was in flower at the time, and the discovery that the ratio was almost exactly 50:50. The flowers are small but charming, the gutter-shaped labellum embraced by the other coherent perianth segments. The edge of the labellum is frilled and the central part of the gutter is full of glistening green nectar. The scent is sweet and surprisingly strong for such a small flower.

Pollination is effected by bumblebees (*Bombus* sp.), and at least two species are involved.

Seed production is good and accounts for most new plants, since vegetative multiplication by the development of lateral buds is slow. It was thought that plants took upwards of thirteen years to reach maturity from seed, but under laboratory conditions (T. Wells et al), flowering plants have been produced in five years, albeit that they have proved to be rather dumpy specimens.

Autumn Lady's-tresses is usually to be found on old chalk pastures or calcareous grassland, and will flourish on cliff-tops near the sea. It is widespread in Sussex, particularly on the chalk downs between Brighton and Eastbourne, and appears throughout Sussex in lawns and cemeteries, possibly brought in with imported turf.

It flowers from mid-August to the end of September. Apparent dramatic fluctuations in numbers of flowering plants do not necessarily indicate fluctuations in the total population. Many, if not most, of the mature plants in a colony are non-flowering, but since the leaves are gone by flowering time, the flat, non-flowering rosettes are very hard to detect.

There are no hybrids, and no varieties of Autumn Lady's-tresses have been described.

10 COMMON TWAYBLADE

Listera ovata (L.) R.Brown

Common Twayblade is the most widespread orchid in Sussex, often flowering in considerable quantity. The earliest record I can find is a herbarium sheet in the Natural History Museum collected in St.Leonard's Forest by J.T. Syme in June 1834. Many of the botanists of past times did not bother to collect it, regarding it as too common to be worth the trouble, but strangely the next oldest record is by another member of the same family, J.B. Syme in April 1866, who collected his specimen from Bramber Castle

I must admit a liking for a species which is often thought of as rather dull. The stem can be as tall as 75cm, covered thickly in glandular hairs, with two dark green oval leaves borne some way up the stem. There are usually two opposite leaves, hence the common name, which is probably derived from the Old Norse, since in modern Swedish it is Tvåblad. Occasionally plants will have a third leaf above the pair, and I have found one plant bearing five leaves on the stem. Blind stems occur fairly frequently, consisting of two leaves with no flowering stem above them.

The open flower spike may have as many as a hundred yellow-green flowers, the outer and upper perianth segments forming a hood above the long labellum, which is forked almost to mid-way. The base of the labellum is grooved and secretes nectar. The ovary is globular and borne on a fairly long pedicel.

Pollination is effected by male sawflies of the species *Tenthredo atra*, male Springtails *Apteris abdominator* and male ichneumons *Ichneumon insidiosus* which are active in May and June. The rostellum is fragile and explodes on contact, glueing pollen to the insect's head and frightening it away to another flower. After the pollinia have been removed, the rostellum hinges up to expose the stigma, the time lapse ensuring cross-pollination. Bees visit the flowers for nectar, but do not act as pollinators.

Seed production is very efficient. Plants also develop buds on the branching rhizomes, and can be seen as a line of individuals of decreasing maturity stretching away from the parent plant.

Common Twayblade flowers from late April until July, the later dates being for plants growing in shade. It is immensely tolerant, growing on chalk or base-rich soils in dense woodland or on open sunny downland slopes where the plants are usually shorter and more compact. It is widely distributed across all of East and West Sussex, and in some woodland can be so numerous as to be the dominant ground plant over a considerable area.

No hybrids are known.

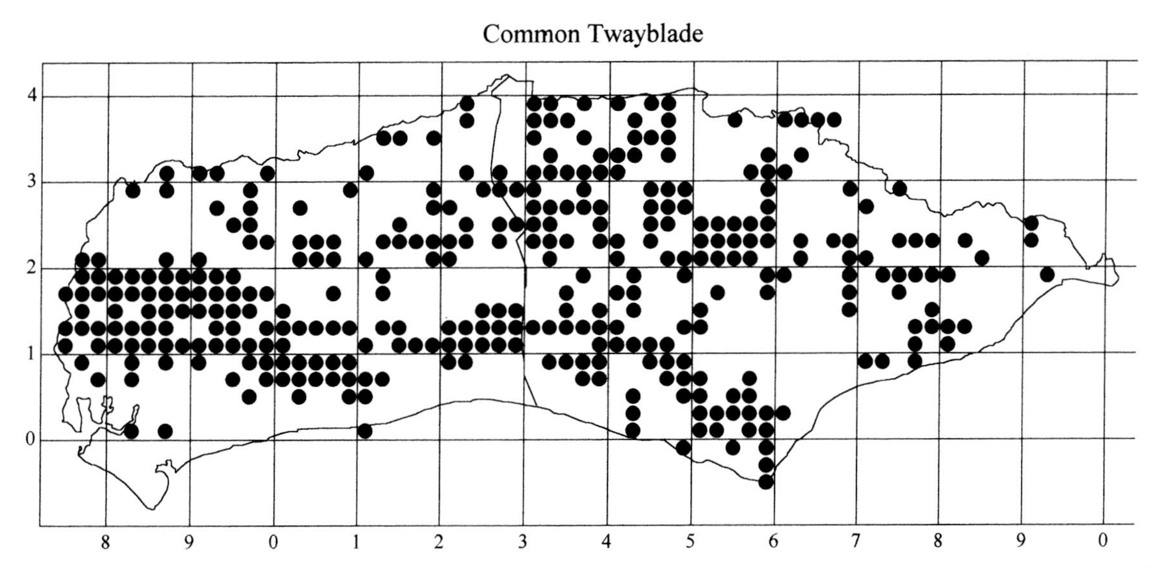

11 LESSER TWAYBLADE

Listera cordata (L.) R.Brown

The history of Lesser Twayblade in Sussex is unusual, especially when you consider its distribution in Britain. The nearest other records are in Devon and Somerset to the west, Brecon in Wales and Derbyshire to the north. It grew formerly in the New Forest.

Wolley-Dod (1937) mentions a record for Wolstonbury Hill in 1921, where F.F. Woods of Ditchling said he found it and had the record confirmed by Druce. There is no evidence for this, and it was obviously a mistake. The locality there is so utterly unlike anywhere I have seen it in Britain that it can be discounted.

The other records are less contentious, although no herbarium specimens or photographs appear to exist. The famous nurseryman Will Ingwersen found it in Gravetye Woods, and in 1989 apparently found it in another area of the same woods. It is inconceivable that such a reliable plantsman would mistake the species, but one is left wondering how it came to be there. It is possible that it was introduced in peat, moss or similar material from the north of Britain where the Lesser Twayblade is widespread.

Lesser Twayblade has all the characteristics of its larger, commoner relative, but in every respect these are in miniature. The two heart-shaped leaves are borne some way up the stem, and in the non-flowering plant they closely resemble the first two leaves of young bilberry plants (*Vaccinium myrtillus*), although paler apple-green in colour. The stem is usually about 5cm tall, reddish and covered in fine hairs.

The perianth segments are narrow and blunt, the labellum long and deeply forked. All the floral parts are bronze coloured, and when examined closely appear iridescent and most attractive, despite their diminutive size.

The ovary is globular and slightly ridged. Pollination in most cases appears to be by female gnats *Sciara thomae*, but self-fertilisation may also occur. Seed is set in most capsules.

In the normal part of its range Lesser Twayblade is a plant of acid soils, growing in many

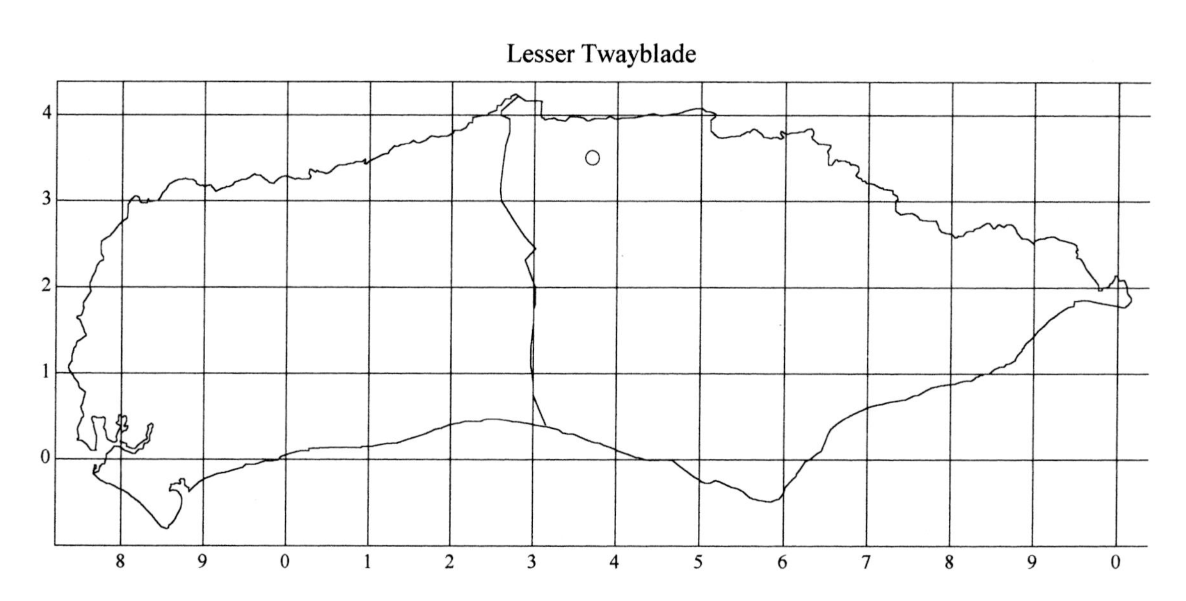

cases in the bog-moss *Sphagnum rubellum*, often under the cover of heather and bilberry. It also grows in pine woods, but always in moss and in damp conditions.

It flowers from mid-May until the end of June. Records for later flowering dates may be due to the persistence of the floral structure, apparently unchanged even when the seed capsule has split and the seed has been dispersed. The flowers still appear to be 'out' when they are in fact 'over'.

It is a tiny plant and easily overlooked. Its rediscovery in Sussex would be very welcome.

12 BIRD'S-NEST ORCHID

Neottia nidus-avis (L.) Richard

The first record for Bird's-nest Orchid appears in Wolley-Dod as 1724, when 'Mr Manningham recorded it in several woods in Sussex,' as noted in Ray's Synopsis Methodica Stirpium (3rd edition), and then H.C. Watson from Arundel in 1806. Thereafter there is a gap until the mid 19th century, when there is a cluster of collections, chiefly from West Sussex, beginning with W.W. Newbould from Goodwood in June 1843 and F.C.S. Roper from Netherfield in 1875. Guermonprez also knew it from Goodwood, and there are some paintings in Portsmouth Museum which he made in 1891 and 1893.

The true rhizomes of Bird's-nest Orchid are concealed in the tangled mass of short, fleshy roots which give the plant its name. Both roots and rhizomes are heavily infected with mycorrhizal fungus upon which the plant is totally dependent, since it has no chlorophyll to perform photosynthesis and is wholly saprophytic.

The stem is 20-50cm tall, the lower part bearing a number of primitive sheath-like leaves and scales. All parts are honey-brown in colour. The flowering spike is robust, with a dense mass of as many as one hundred flowers. The dead flowering stem of the previous year will often persist alongside the new flower spike. The perianth segments form a loose hood above the broad, forked labellum, the lobes of which are rounded and divergent. At the base of the labellum is a shallow cup which secretes nectar and functions as a primitive spur. The flowers have a sweet scent and attract insects, especially male red ants *Myrmica rubra*.

The pollen masses are yellow and very friable, and like those of Common Twayblade (*Listera ovata*) they explode on contact and glue pollen material onto the visiting insect. Self-fertilisation also occurs and N. Bernard has recorded flowers that were not only cleistogamous, but actually set seed in spikes which, for various reasons, had failed to emerge from the soil. Seed production is efficient, plants reaching maturity after about nine years.

The Bird's-nest Orchid flowers from the end of April until the end of June, being at its best in the last week of May. It is widespread throughout Sussex, especially in beech woods on the chalk. It flourishes best in warm, wet conditions, and was particularly fine and abundant in the spring of 2000. It needs mature woodland, and does not take kindly to intense competition from other plants, doing best in shade on barish ground under the beeches, where the roots can spread through the deep litter of rotting leaves.

It has been lost from many sites in East Sussex where woodland has been felled and cleared, but it is still abundant in the downland woods of West Sussex.

There are no known variants or hybrids.

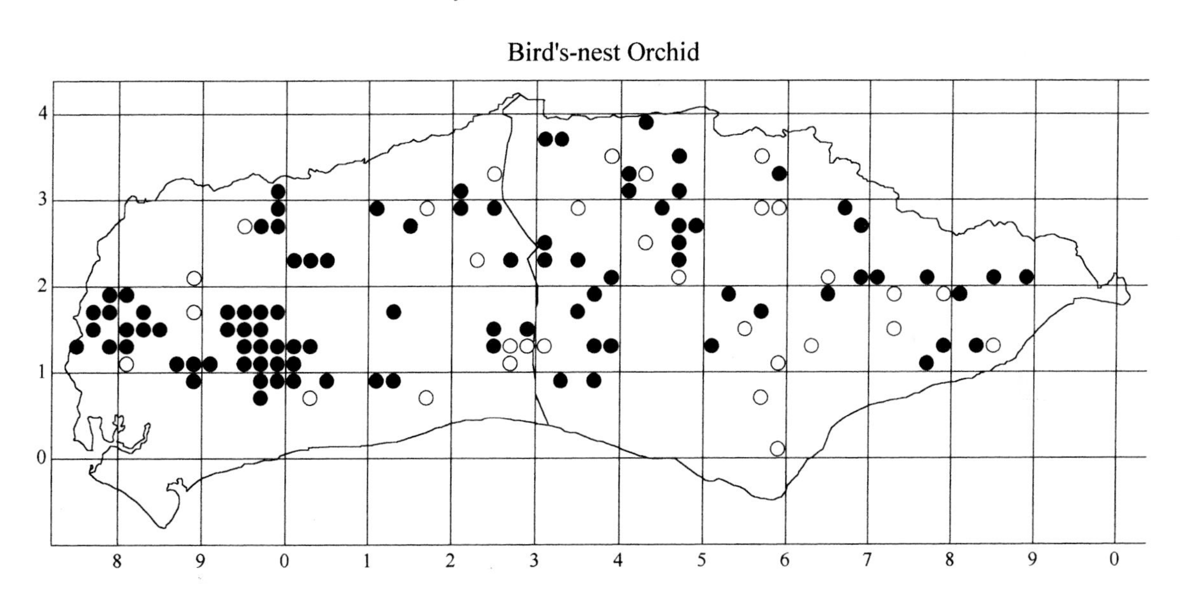

13 BOG ORCHID

Hammarbya paludosa (L.) Kuntze
[*Malaxis paludosa* (L.) Swartz]

The very first mention of Bog Orchid in Sussex is by Ray in 1680, 'in the bog near the windmill in Frant Forest'. The plants were rediscovered by J. Sharp in 1844, and one collection made by a Mrs Jenner is in Watson's herbarium at Kew, where he writes 'Bog behind the plantation by Broadwater Forest towards Harrison's Rocks. No doubt this was inclosed in Ray's days and in all probability it was his place'.

Apart from the Ashdown Forest area, there are old collections from 'Barnett's Rough', Duncton Common, which Rev F.H. Arnold visited, at the age of 22, in July 1853. It saddens me to see a sheet bearing a dozen dried specimens in his herbarium. Modern maps show the area as a part of Lavington Common, which has been drained and afforested. F.C.S. Roper found it at Balcombe in 1865, and there is a dubious record from near Pulborough.

Otherwise most records come from the area on and around Ashdown Forest. During preparation of the excellent Flora of Ashdown Forest (1996) a great deal of work was done in searching archives and looking at every possible location for the Bog Orchid. It was well known in 'the great bog at Kidbrooke Park', at Pressbridge Warren near Nutley, and in a bog near Hartfield – all mid-19th century records – with visits by Deakin in 1871, Arnold in 1877, C.E. Salmon in 1895 (sheet in the Natural History Museum) and Thomas Hilton in 1899.

Most fascinating is the story of George Dent, who lived near Wych Cross and made detailed records of a site from 1920 to 1952. I can do no better than quote from the text of the Flora, as recorded by one of the authors, Tim Rich: 'By a series of coincidences his (George Dent's) diary has been traced. Tim Rich's grandmother shared a nursing home at Midhurst with Lady Stratton, whose sister, Phyllis Green, lived next door to George Dent near Wych Cross and inherited the diary when he died in 1959. It gives a breathtaking, detailed account of the two sites and the plants between 1928 and 1952. George was obviously fascinated with the plants and visited them regularly, observing flowering, fruiting and the bulbils on the leaves. He used binoculars to spot the plants, and notes having bare feet in the marshes.'

Oliver Buckle last saw the Bog Orchid on Ashdown Forest in 1952, and that is the last written record. Possibly the last time it flowered was in 1956, when George Dent took Phyllis and Robert Green to see them, after which they seem to have disappeared. Many careful searches have all been in vain.

The Bog Orchid is tiny (3-12cm high) all green and very difficult to see in the sphagnum moss in which it grows. The roots are reduced to fine hairs heavily infected with mycorrhizum. At the base of the stem are two pseudobulbs, one above the other, formed by swellings of the stem. The upper pseudobulb carries two sheathing leaves and there are two to four small, oval leaves near the middle of the stem. On the leaf margins there may be a fringe of tiny bulbils, which break off and form new plants.

The stem is five-angled, with up to fifteen tiny green flowers with a minute bract at the base of each. The flowers are unique among British orchids, in that the labellum is always uppermost, since the flowers rotate through 360° during development, so that the labellum returns to its primitive dorsal position. Careful examination of the labellum will reveal that it has alternate pale and dark green longitudinal stripes. All the other perianth segments are green and minute, the inner segments tending to fold round the back of the flower.

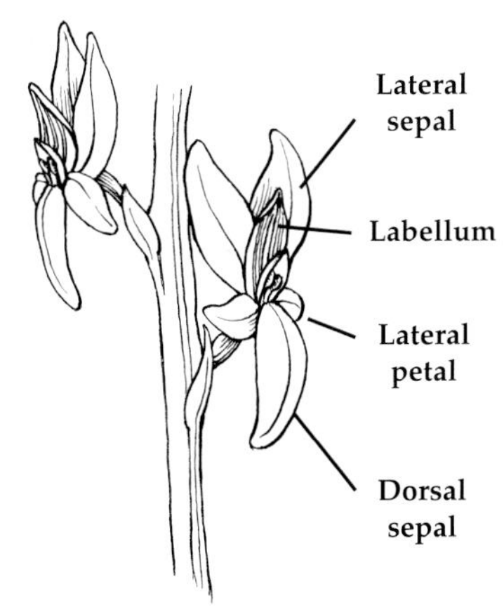

Enlarged flowers of Bog Orchid.

Pollination is probably due to the activity of a gnat *Sciara thomae*, or to the small flies which are all too plentiful in bogs. Seed is set in good quantity and, because it is extremely light, floats away on the surface water.

The Bog Orchid requires a fairly extensive cushion of sphagnum moss in which to grow, and a habitat which is constantly wet, with an acid pH. Unfortunately in Sussex such habitat has almost gone as a result of drainage, afforestation and alteration in climate, and it is most unlikely that we shall see this delightful miniature orchid in the county in the future. There remains a remote chance that it could still turn up on Duncton Common and near the Isle of Thorns on Ashdown Forest.

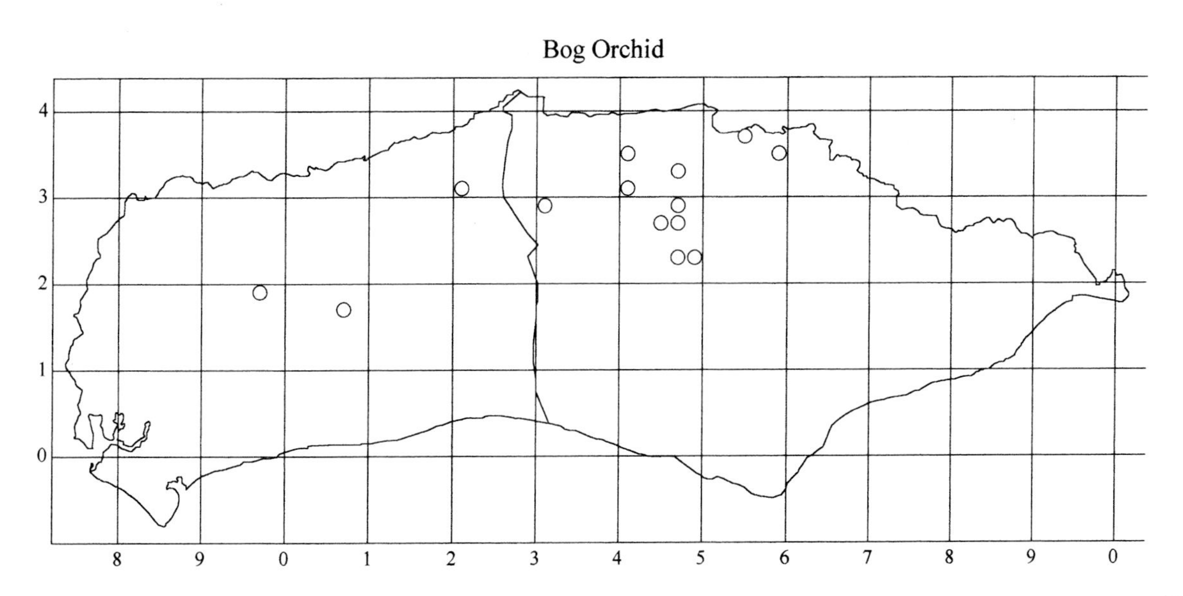

14 MUSK ORCHID

Herminium monorchis (L.) R.Brown

There is something rather endearing about a plant whose common and scientific names are both hopelessly misleading. The Musk Orchid certainly does not smell of musk, and it does not have a single rounded tuber as the Latin name would suggest, but one main tuber from which the flowering stem arises, with a further four or five smaller tubers carried on fine stalks. If the plant is pulled up, these stalks break off, so the plant appears to have just the one tuber.

Musk Orchid was first noted in Sussex in 1790, with the first documented record in 1805 from near a public house called the Marquis of Blandford, in Worthing. The specimen was collected by a Mr Jackson and is in Sowerby's herbarium. There is an undated specimen in Borrer's herbarium collected for him at Harting by a Mr Weaver, and several specimens in F.C.S. Roper's herbarium collected in 1865 and 1867 from the downs above Westmeston Church – a place at which it still grows.

The Musk Orchid is small, 5-15cm tall, with leaves and flowers all bright yellow-green. There are several strap-shaped basal leaves and a single pointed stem leaf. The bracts equal the ovaries. The flower spike is densely packed with twenty or more tiny flowers. All the perianth segments are pointed and toothed and the labellum is short and three-lobed. At the base of the labellum is a cup-shaped hollow which secretes nectar, and the flowers have a sweet honey scent.

Although most Musk Orchids are small, there are two spikes in Wolley-Dod's herbarium which were collected at Graffham chalkpit in 1902. They are 26cm and 30cm tall, a height I have never seen anywhere in over fifty years of orchid study, and each bears hundreds of flowers.

Each of the pollinia has a large round viscidium. The flowers are so constructed that visiting insects can only get in sideways, when the viscidium sticks on to a leg. Pollination by small insects is frequent. A tiny soldier beetle *Malthodes pumilus* and an equally tiny parasitic wasp T*etrastichus diaphantus* may be involved, but their identification is by no means certain. Flowers can also be self-fertilising. In any event seed is set abundantly.

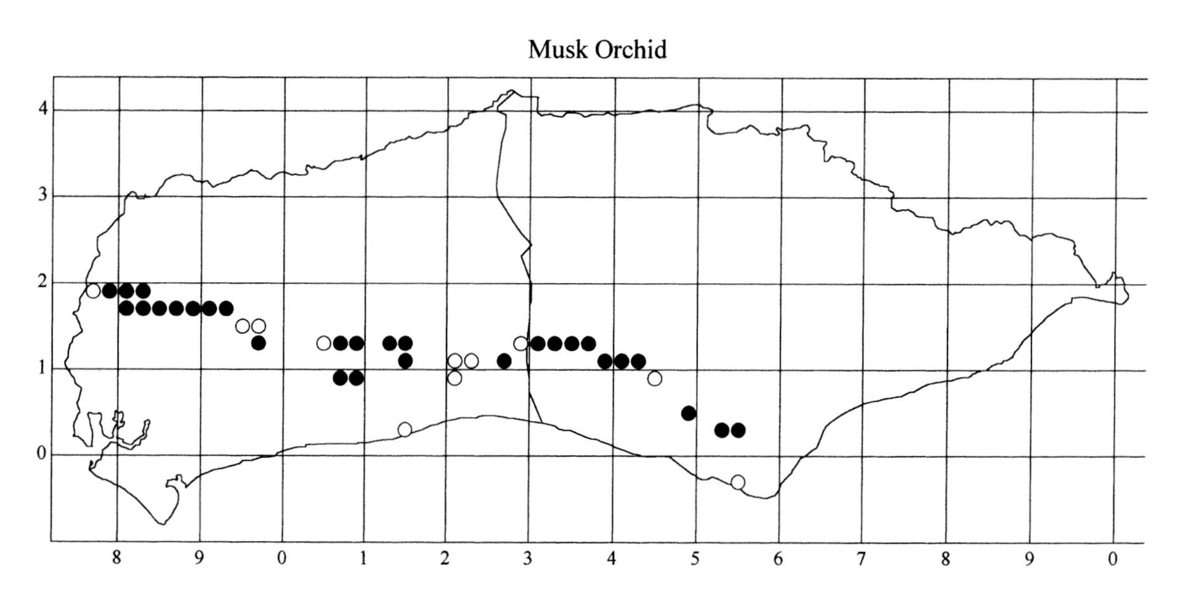

The Musk Orchid in Sussex is restricted to short grassland on the chalk, and follows the line of the South Downs in its distribution. It particularly favours the terracettes produced on slopes by the feet of grazing sheep, and likes a sunny aspect. However it is very shallow rooted and can suffer in a prolonged drought. At Malling Down nature reserve I counted over 20,000 flowering spikes, some growing in clumps of more than twenty, during the summer of 1966. Thanks to the drought of summer 1976 there were none at all the following year, and numbers have never recovered above a couple of hundred since then.

Despite this, the Musk Orchid is remarkably persistent, and it still grows in many of the sites recorded by botanists such as Arnold, Roper and Hilton in the mid-1800s. It remains plentiful in some years at Heyshott and Didling Downs, but has been overgrown east of Harting Hill, and was destroyed by ploughing at Bepton some time in the 1960s. In Kent and Surrey it occurs at a number of sites on the North Downs, and very locally in Hampshire, the Cotswolds and the Chilterns, but no further north.

It flowers from mid-June to the early part of August. No variants or hybrids are known.

15 FROG ORCHID

Coeloglossum viride (L.) Hartman
[*Habenaria viridis* (L.) R.Brown]

To the Frog Orchid may belong the honour of being the first orchid in Sussex to appear in print, named by C. Merrett in 1666 as Orchis Batrachoides autumnalis flore Luteo, growing near Lewes.

This would suggest that the 'frog' name was current in the seventeenth century – Batrachoides meaning frog-like – although outwardly the orchid seems to have little in common with its namesake. The strap-shaped labellum, faintly three-lobed at the tip, does bear a faint resemblance to a frog's tongue, but the Greek scientific name *Coeloglossum* translates as 'hollow tongue'.

The first record noted in Wolley-Dod (1937) is for 1805 and next is a herbarium specimen of 1813 collected for William Borrer by the indefatigable Mr Weaver from 'near Harting'. There are many mid- to late-19th century records. Rev F.H. Arnold found it at Fishbourne Church Field in 1852 and again in 1875, when he also recorded it from Goodwood racecourse. Deakin found it in meadows between High Rocks and Groombridge in 1871, and C.A. Wright from Cow Down near Pyecombe in 1888, where it certainly persisted to 1937 when Ursula Smith recorded it there. The Frog Orchid has two palmate tubers, which when mature appear to be free of mycorrhizal fungus. The stem is 5-35cm, slightly angled and often tinged rusty red in colour. There are three to five broadly strap-shaped basal leaves and several pointed stem leaves. The lower bracts are longer, and the upper bracts shorter than the flowers, which may number more than fifty in some large spikes.

The flowers are usually yellow-green, but in drier sites, certainly in calcareous sand dunes in north and west Britain, the entire flower spike can be a rich, reddish brown. The outer and inner perianth segments form a neat, rounded hood above the paler, strap-shaped labellum. The pollinia are yellow and club-shaped. When detached they slowly pivot forward, so helping cross-fertilisation.

Small insects probably act as pollinators, and the click beetle *Athous haemorrhoidalis* has been observed with pollinia stuck to its head. Seed production is efficient and vegetative reproduction does not appear to be of any importance.

The first leaves appear about two or three years after seed is set, and I have recorded individual plants flowering consistently for more than seven seasons.

Frog Orchids flower from late June to early September, with the occasional plant found in flower as early as the end of May, especially near the sea in the area around Beachy Head. I have certainly seen this on a number of occasions, and there is a herbarium sheet of F.C. Roper collected at Belle Tout dated 26th May 1878.

Like the Musk Orchid, the distribution of the Frog Orchid follows the line of the chalk downs from West Sussex to Beachy Head, and in all sites it favours short downland turf, especially on old chalk workings and around prehistoric barrows. In such places it can be abundant, with over 800 in flower around the rim of an old dewpond near Burpham in 1993.

Numbers do vary greatly from year to year, but it seems to be holding its own in the county. It is strange that it does so well in Sussex, yet in Kent, with plenty of apparently suitable habitat, it is a plant of extreme rarity, with one site near Dover. It is also rare in Surrey, but more frequent in Hampshire.

Numerous records of hybrids with spotted and marsh orchids, Fragrant Orchid (*Gymnadenia conopsea*) and Lesser Butterfly-orchid (*Platanthera bifolia*) are known elsewhere in Britain but not in Sussex. The nearest we have is of the apparent hybrid *Coeloglossum viride* x *Dactylorhiza praetermissa*, collected just over the border in Hampshire by Col Godfery, and photographed by E.J. Bedford in 1917.

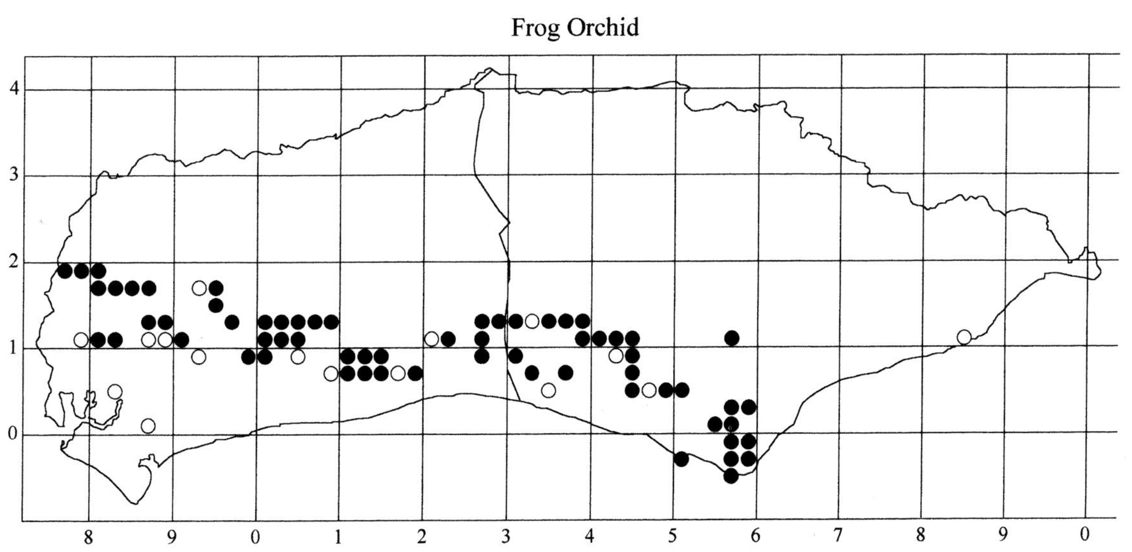

16 FRAGRANT ORCHID

Gymnadenia conopsea (L.) R.Brown
[*Habenaria conopsea* (L.) Bentham]

The Fragrant Orchid was first noted in 1786 growing on the downs between Lewes and Offham, with the first herbarium specimen dating from 1816. Most herbaria I have examined from the late 19th century have collections, such as one in Arnold's herbarium made by Mr Unwin in 1853 from Lewes downs, and many sheets in F.C.S. Roper's herbarium - Folkington in 1874, Filching in 1881 and Eastdean in 1882.

Fragrant Orchid has deeply divided palmate tubers, and a stem which in most grassland plants is 15-20cm in height. There are three to five long, narrow, folded basal leaves and several narrow, pointed stem leaves. The bracts are equal to, or shorter than, the flowers.

The flower spike may have as many as 200 densely packed pink, sweetly scented flowers. The oblong lateral sepals project outwards and downwards, the upper sepal and two upper inner perianth segments forming a loose hood. The labellum is flat and three-lobed, with a long, down-curving, slender spur. White flowers are not uncommon.

Pollination is carried out mainly by moths, which have the long proboscis needed to reach the nectar in the spur, while male Large Skipper (*Ochlodes venata*) and male Six-spot Burnet (*Zygaena filipendula*) also regularly act as pollinators. Bees certainly visit the flowers, often falling prey to the various species of crab spiders which commonly lurk in the Fragrant Orchid flowers.

Seed is set in good quantity and plants may sometimes flower as soon as three years after this, although the normal period is probably more like five years.

Three distinct forms of the Fragrant Orchid exist, with different habitat requirements, morphology, colour, scent and flowering dates. Both Dr Francis Rose and Simon Davey have noted hybrids which on occasion prove infertile, suggesting that the three forms merit full specific rank, rather than the sub-specific rank usually afforded. All three forms occur in Sussex, and for the moment I have dealt with them as sub-species.

Gymnadenia conopsea ssp.***conopsea***

This form (*right, and on facing page*) is a plant of calcareous or limestone grassland, and in Sussex is widely distributed along the downs from the west of Sussex to Beachy Head, with a scattering of sites near Rye in the far east of the county. It also occurs further north in a few sites in East Sussex, in meadows and on road verges.

The flower spike is of moderate size, up to 20cm or so, and the flowers are fairly well spaced. The lateral sepals are pointed oblong, and slope slightly downwards. The labellum is divided into three well developed, rounded lobes, the central lobe longer than the lateral lobes. The spur is long, thin and downcurved. The scent is sweetish, although to some individuals it may seem a trifle rancid. Flowering occurs from the end of May to the end of July.

Gymnadenia conopsea ssp.***densiflora*** (Wahlenb.) E.G.Camus, Bergon & A.Camus

This form is classically a plant of calcareous fens, but also grows on north-facing downland slopes. It can be massive, up to 75cm tall, with many basal stem leaves and a densely packed spike of large flowers. The flowers can vary in colour from pale mauve to dark pink, and are sweetly carnation scented. The lateral sepals are blunt and point sideways. The labellum is broad and skirt-like, the two lateral lobes larger than the rather poorly differentiated centre lobe. The flowers are at their best in July and early August, later than the common form.

This form occurs at Balcombe and was well known from Aldermere, where Arnold collected it in July 1882 and Guermonprez painted it in July 1921. Plants which very closely resemble it

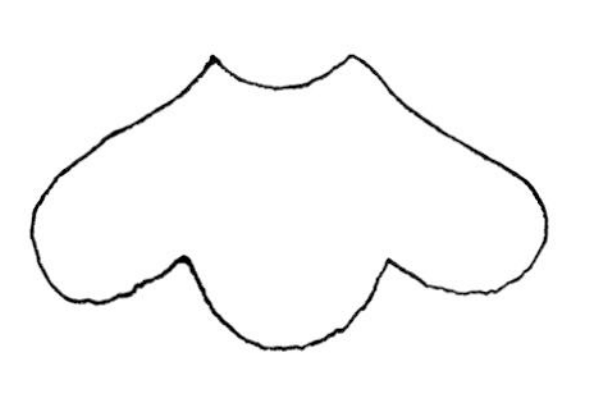

Normal form

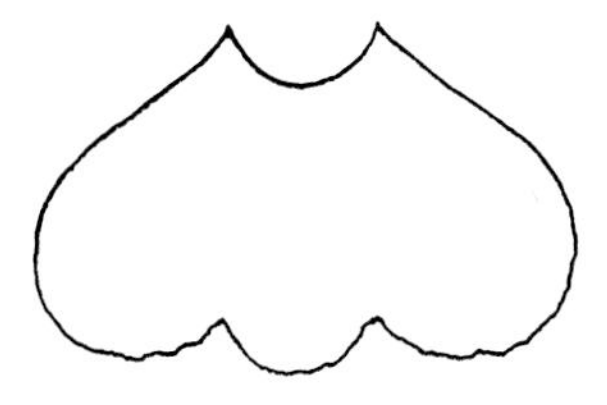

ssp. *densiflora*

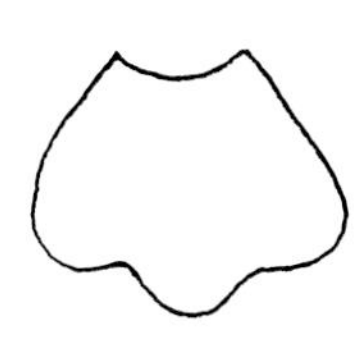

ssp. *borealis*

frequently occur on north-facing downland slopes, both in West Sussex and between Ditchling Beacon and Plumpton.

Gymnadenia conopsea ssp.***borealis*** (Druce) F. Rose

Despite the scientific name, and its British distribution north to Scotland, this form is far more widely spread in Europe than ssp.*conopsea*, being found as far south as the Dordogne in France. In Britain it is a plant of lime-deficient pastures in the north and west.

There is a collection by H.C. Watson in July 1842 from near Nutley windmill, which is in his herbarium at Kew. There is also a record for 'Downs in Sussex' in the Reynolds herbarium in Portsmouth Museum, dated July 1922. It was next recorded near Coleman's Hatch in July 1962, but all the flowers were picked. Roger Tallach refound it in 1986, and another site on Ashdown Forest is known.

In 1990 I found a small group of ssp.*borealis* on the downs near Beddingham, and two other downland sites have since been discovered near Plumpton and Folkington. The plants are small,

Ssp. *densiflora* of the Fragrant Orchid *(left)* is a plant of calcareous fens which also grows on north-facing downland slopes. Ssp. *borealis (above)* is a plant of lime-deficient pastures in north and west Britain, but has been found on the Sussex Downs.

flowering in late July and early August, with small, mauve coloured flowers which are carnation scented. The diagnostic features are the shorter spur, and the disproportionately small labellum, which has small side lobes and a longer centre lobe.

Dr Rose maintains that the three taxa of *G. conopsea* are usually quite distinct in morphology and in the habitat they occupy. On Ditchling Beacon ssp. *densiflora* grows on the steep slopes, probably flushed with sub-surface water, while ssp. *conopsea* is confined to flatter, drier ground. On Heyshott Down the population is pure ssp. *densiflora* with no ssp. *conopsea* nearby. Intermediate forms do exist, however – certainly this is true at Beddingham – these presumed hybrids lending weight to the argument that the three taxa merit specific rank.

The Fragrant Orchid hybridises fairly readily, and hybrids are known with Small-white Orchid (*Pseudorchis albida*), Common Spotted-orchid (*Dactylorhiza fuchsii*), Heath Spotted-orchid (*Dactylorhiza maculata* ssp.*ericetorum*), Southern Marsh-orchid (*Dactylorhiza praetermissa*), Northern Marsh-orchid (*D.purpurella*), Frog Orchid (*Coeloglossum viride*) and Pyramidal Orchid (*Anacamptis pyramidalis*). The hybrid with Common Spotted-orchid is the only one which has been recorded in Sussex, and is not uncommon.

A strange peloric form was found on the downs near Lewes in 1970 by a Dutch botanist, Michiel Ebbens. Both inner and outer perianth segments were long and pointed, with just a suggestion of side lobes, and were arranged symmetrically like a six-pointed star.

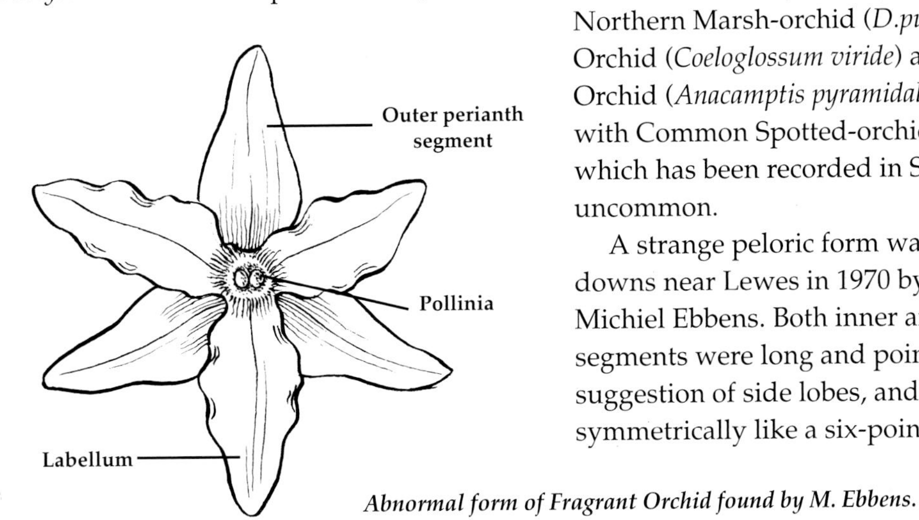

Abnormal form of Fragrant Orchid found by M. Ebbens.

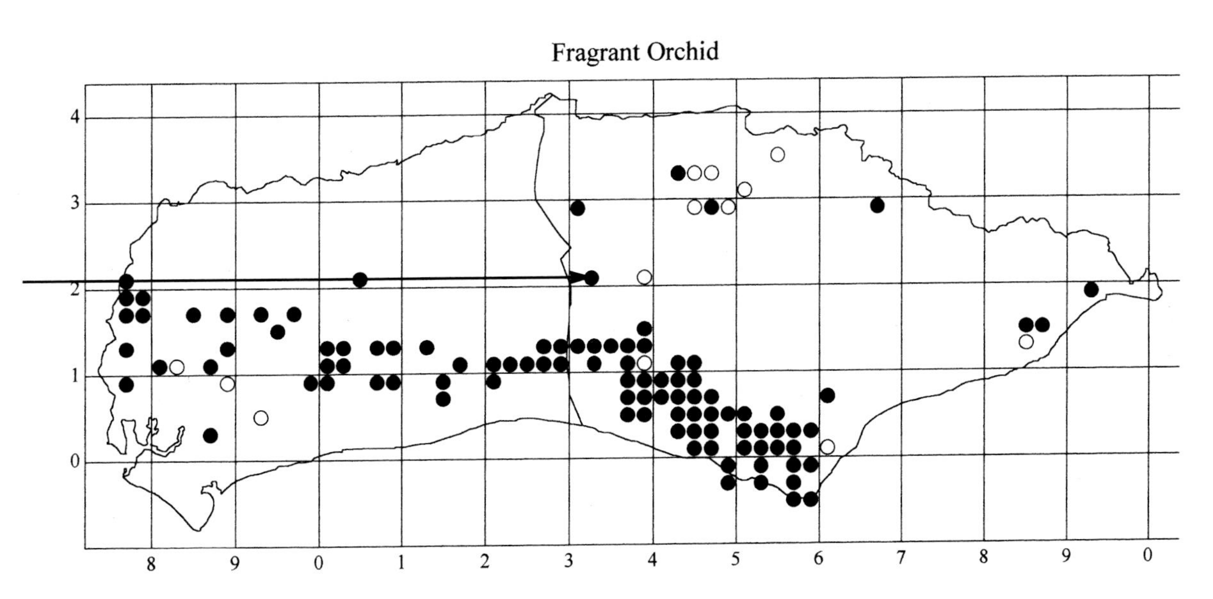

17 SMALL-WHITE ORCHID

Pseudorchis albida (L.) A&D. Loeve
[*Leucorchis albida* (L.) E. Meyer
Gymnadenia albida (L.) Richard
Habenaria albida (L.) R.Brown]

The first record for Small-white Orchid is uncertain. In Babington's memoirs there is a note 'went to St. Leonard's and Tilgate Forests and found *Habenaria brachyglopa*.' Ted Lousley could not trace this synonym, and noted that Babington had collected both the butterfly-orchids there.

There is a sheet in the Kew Herbarium collected by J. Woods (probably Sir Joseph Woods) in 1839 between Fairwarp and Nutley. Also in the Kew Herbarium are two sheets of Small-white Orchid collected by H.C. Watson in 1840 and 1841 from 'northern hillside above the stone pits near Nutley Windmill, Ashdown Forest'. In 1852 Lloyd and McEnnes found it in plenty in an open part of Worth Forest.

The next collection appears to be in 1867 from the same site (J. Edwards). Deakin in 1871 mentions it as from 'Ashdown Forest near Nutleycollected by J.J. Woods, and there is a sheet for 1891 from Nutley in the Natural History Museum labelled J. Woods. Sir Joseph Woods (see **Botanologia**) died in 1864, so the J.J. Woods and J. Woods of these later collections cannot be him, but may refer to one person.

There are a number of accredited collections from locations stretching from Tunbridge Wells and Eridge to Worth and Tilgate Forests, Horsted Keynes and Hartfield. St Leonard's, Tilgate and Worth Forests nowadays bear no resemblance to their former state – a mosaic of lightly grazed grasslands and small woods essential to the requirements of the Small-white Orchid.

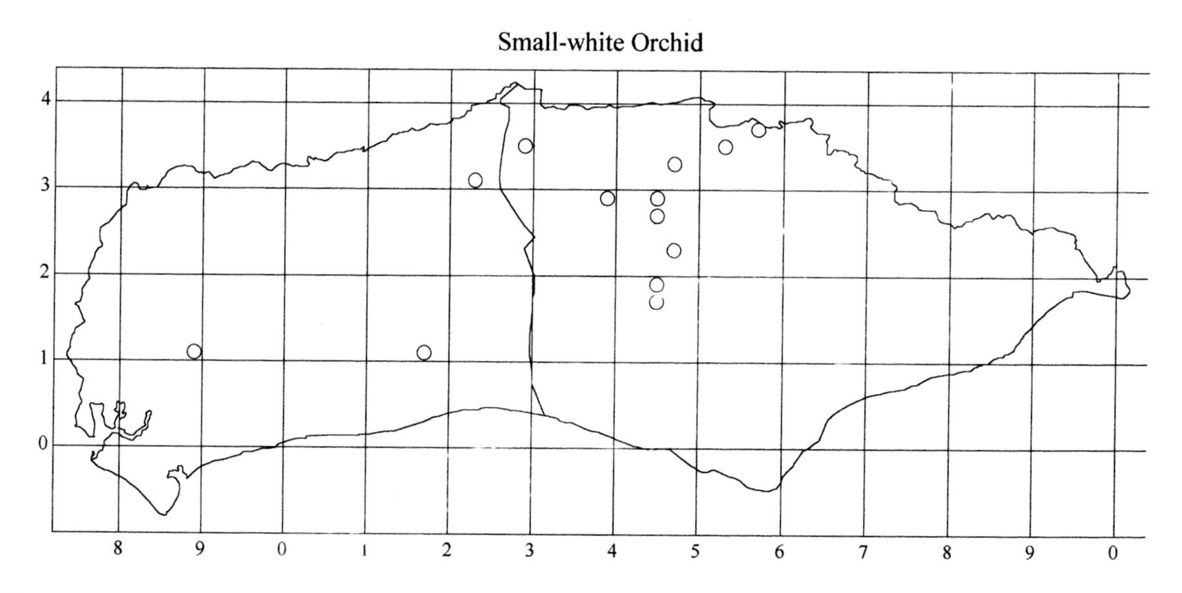

A collection by H.W. Pugsley from the downs west of Bramber on July 17, 1895, appears to be Small-white Orchid, although I was not able to soak off a floret to examine it properly. The spike was curiously sparse (ten flowers) and the flowers were larger than normal. Wolley-Dod notes it as found near Goodwood, but C.B. Tahourdin was unable to confirm this record. E.J. Bedford clearly knew it near Nutley, but unfortunately he kept no written record of the site, which was probably in an old pasture near Nutley windmill. Characteristically, he would tell no one, and the site was later destroyed.

A sheet in the Natural History Museum collected on June 10, 1913, by Mrs Godden is certainly Small-white Orchid, but the site – 'Heath 1.5 miles South of Tunbridge Wells' – is not identified. A 1935 record south of Forest Row is unreliable. In 1943 Dr Francis Rose and John Lavender, botanising near Chuck Hatch, found what they felt was probably this species in a non-flowering state. This could well have been the last sighting of Small-white Orchid in Sussex. A recent record on a north-facing slope above Alciston turned out to be a white Pyramidal Orchid (*Anacamptis pyramidalis*). It would seem that we have lost this delightful species from Sussex.

Small-white Orchid is a charming plant 10-40cm tall, with two small pointed tubers and true roots which spread horizontally near the surface. There are four to six broad,flattened, oval base leaves, and several pointed stem leaves. The bracts are narrow and pointed. The flower spike is cylindrical with usually some twenty small, bell-shaped flowers tightly packed on the stem. Outer and inner perianth segments are short and blunt, forming a small hood, while the labellum is small, with three pointed lobes. There is a short spur.

The creamy white flowers are vanilla scented and attract butterflies, day-flying moths and solitary bees, although no species have been positively identified. Seed is set efficiently and aerial shoots are formed in about four years.

The Small-white Orchid is usually a plant of hill pastures and mountain ledges, both on calcareous and non-calcareous soils, in sunny situations. The flowering period is from the end of May to mid-July in the far north of Britain. Today it is not known south of mid-Wales and the Yorkshire Pennine meadows, but there is an old record for East Kent near Lyminge.

Hybrids with the Fragrant Orchid (*Gymnadenia conopsea*) are known, but have not occurred in Sussex.

18 GREATER BUTTERFLY-ORCHID

Platanthera chlorantha (Custer) Reichenbach
[*Habenaria virescens* Druce
Habenaria chlorantha (Custer) Babington]

The first note of Greater Butterfly-orchid in Sussex is in 1784 from Stansted Forest on the extreme west boundary of the county. Thereafter the first herbarium specimen I can find is in William Borrer's collection, found for him by Mr Weaver at Harting. There is a fine specimen in the Natural History Museum from Alciston, collected in 1827 from a wood where it still flourishes. Both F.C.S. Roper and Thomas Hilton record it many times in the late 1800s from Newtimber, Stanmer Park and Abbott's Wood. There is a particularly fine painting by Guermonprez dated 1893 of a plant from Cocking, and it is obvious from both Arnold's Flora of 1887 and Wolley-Dod (1937) that it was not uncommon across most of Sussex at that time.

The Greater Butterfly-orchid has two parsnip-shaped tubers and a number of thin horizontal roots. The stem is 20-60cm, the taller plants occurring in shaded woodland. Size does not differentiate between the two butterfly-orchid species. The two broad leaves are large, pale green and shiny on the upper surface, and often suffer damage from slugs. There are several stem leaves, and long pointed bracts which equal the long and slightly S-shaped ovaries.

The spike is large, with ten to twenty large, well-spaced, white flowers, which stand out well in the gloom of the woods. The two lateral outer perianth segments are broad and pointed, wavy edged, and droop downwards. The upper outer segment and the inner segments form a broad loose hood, with the long strap-shaped labellum hanging down like a tongue. The spur is very long, projecting across the flower spike to the opposite side, and curves downwards almost in a semi-circle. It is translucent, so that the nectar in it is clearly visible.

At the mouth of the spur are the two pollinia, whose appearance is distinctive and a reliable way to separate this species from the Lesser Butterfly-orchid (*Platanthera bifolia*). In the Greater Butterfly-orchid they are set wide apart on either side of the spur entrance and converge dorsally, but do not meet. The viscidia are large and round, set on either side like the headphones on a personal stereo, the object being to stick to the sides of the head of a visiting insect. The differences between Greater and Lesser Butterfly-orchids are described under the latter species.

The scent is sweet and powerful, and being stronger at night attracts mainly night-flying moths. Silver-Y moths (*Autographa monoglypha*), Elephant Hawk-moth (*Deilephila elpenor*) and

Small Elephant Hawk-moth (*D.porcellus*) have all been recorded acting as pollinators. Bumblebees also visit the flowers, but may not pollinate them, as the proboscis is too short. After the pollinia are removed they swivel forwards and inwards, so as to contact the stigma of the next flower visited. Seed is set in a high proportion of flowers.

As noted in **Germination and Growth**, Greater Butterfly-orchid can apparently remain in a vegetative, non-flowering, state for many years, coming into flower when woodland is coppiced or felled, and more light is admitted to the site. It flowers in late May and throughout June.

Greater Butterfly-orchid is widely distributed throughout Sussex, and is more frequent in the west of the county, having been lost from more than half of its known sites in East Sussex. It is a slight comfort that a number of flourishing colonies have been found or refound in the east in the last six or seven years. It is a plant mainly of woodlands in Sussex, growing best in light, dappled shade in coppiced woodland or small woods, often on clay soils, but also in beech woods on the chalk and further in old, damp meadows or downland.

Hybrids have not been recorded in Sussex, but a number of peloric forms have occurred, some with no labellum or spur, others with three labella and spurs in place of the normal inner perianth segments.

Greater Butterfly-orchid

19 LESSER BUTTERFLY-ORCHID

Platanthera bifolia (L.) Richard
[*Habenaria bifolia* (L.) R. Brown]

The first note of the species in Sussex is in 1768, with the first record from near Frant in 1816. Arnold (1887) notes it as 'rather common in woods, heaths and boggy places', recording it from Chilgrove,Williams Wood Stoughton, Itchenor and Billingshurst in the west, to Laughton Woods, Catsfield, Guestling, Fairlight, East Grinstead and Ashdown Forest in the east. Thomas Hilton and F.C.S. Roper in the late 1800s collected it in many sites, from Dallington Forest and Ashburnham to Ditchling Common and Clayton Holt. By the time of Wolley-Dod's Flora of Sussex (1937) it had decreased in frequency sufficiently for him to note it as 'occasional but general', with some 34 localities named.

The situation has declined sharply since the 1930s, and it must now be reckoned as a rare species in Sussex, particularly in the east of the county. There have been several welcome records recently in the west, from Stedham, near the Mens, Rewell Wood near Arundel and Inholmes Wood near Kingley Vale, but it has been absent from Ashdown Forest since 1969 and from Chailey Common since 1987. The distribution map must be accepted as over-optimistic, although there is always the hope that it may reappear in some of its old haunts. This depressing picture is common in most counties in the southern half of England.

The Lesser Butterfly-orchid is no smaller than its 'Greater' relative, being 15-55cm in height, but the broad, shiny leaves are proportionately shorter and wider – elliptical rather than oval. The stem carries fifteen to twenty flowers in a spike which may be quite compact in heathland plants or well-spaced in plants from woodlands, but the whole spike is narrower in diameter than *P. chlorantha*.

The sweetly scented white flowers have the same general appearance, with two important differences, which make identification simple. The two pollinia are erect and lie close together, appearing to close the throat of the spur, while the viscidia are small and oval. Secondly, the long

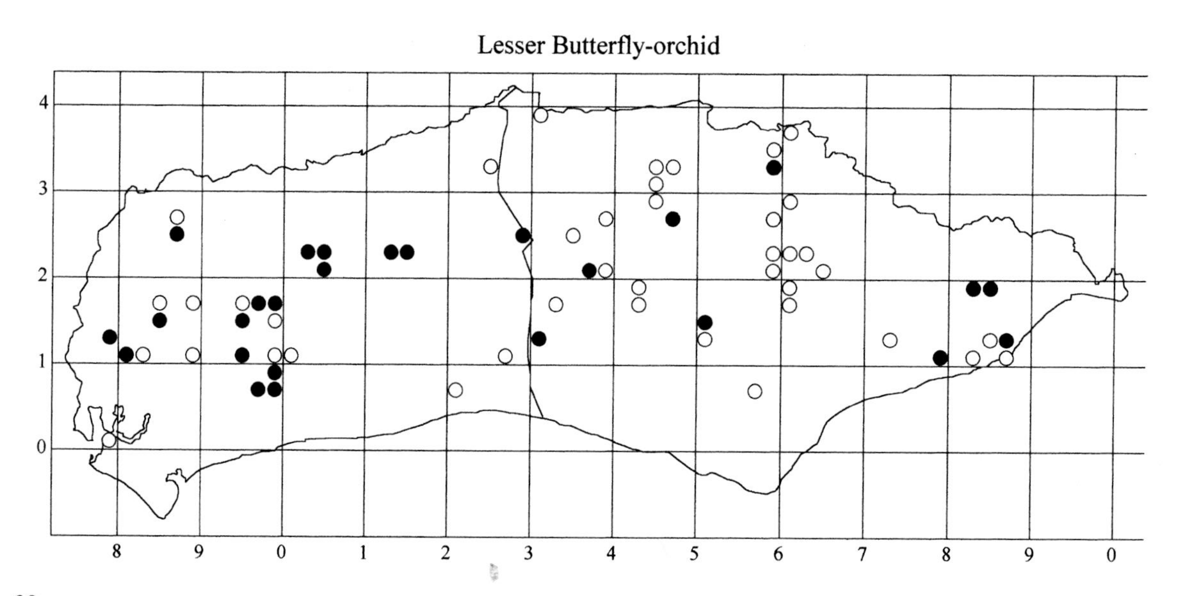

spur projects almost horizontally across the flower spike, and does not curve down as it does in the Greater Butterfly-orchid.

Pollination is similarly effected by night-flying moths, of which the Elephant Hawk-moth (*Dielephila elpenor*), Small Elephant Hawk-moth (*D. porcellus*) and Pine Hawk-moth (*Hyloicus pinastri*) have all been recorded removing pollinia. After a short time interval the pollinia swivel to point forwards,so that they strike the stigma of the next flower to be visited.

Growth from seed follows a similar pattern to that of the Greater Butterfly-orchid, but the species is on the whole much more tolerant of acid conditions, growing on heaths as well as in woodland, on both clay soils and on the chalk.

The Lesser Butterfly-orchid flowers from late May until the end of June in Sussex.

In 1924 at Chilgrove C.B. Tahourdin found a peloric form where the two upper inner perianth segments resembled the outer perianth segments, and did not come to form a hood. I came across the photograph he took of the plant among a collection of E.J. Bedford's prints which turned up in Lewes.

Among them were unlabelled photographs of apparent hybrids of Lesser Butterfly-orchid. The hybrid in photographs Ref:E851 and E852 appears to me to be that of *Platanthera bifolia* x *Dactylorhiza fuchsii*, although Wolley-Dod (p. 482) refers to the hybrid with *Dactylorhiza maculata* ssp. *ericetorum* as coming from Pressridge Warren.

The other photograph Ref:E848 seems to be *Platanthera bifolia* x *Dactylorhiza maculata* ssp. *ericetorum*, and was on Ashdown Forest on June 20, 1931. All of the photographs have been deposited at the Natural History Museum along with Bedford's orchid watercolours.

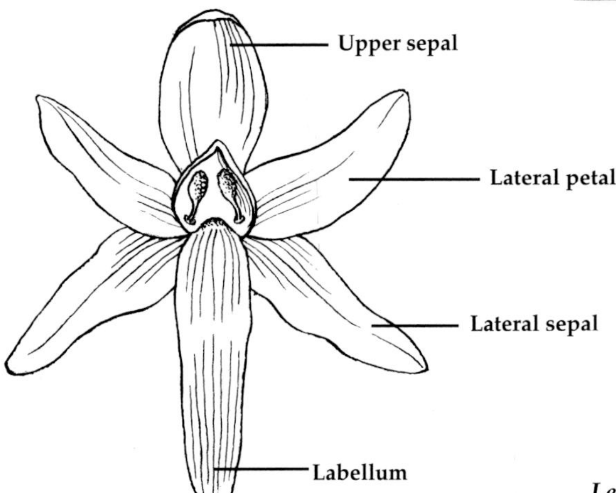

Left: Abnormal Lesser Butterfly-orchid (C.B.Tahourdin).

20 BEE ORCHID

Ophrys apifera Hudson

The first mention of the Bee Orchid in Sussex is in Borrer's The Botanist's Guide in 1805, when it was noted as growing 'on the slopes of the Hill west of Landport, Lewes'. Early writers speak of it as being not uncommon on the chalk from Harting in the west to Battle in the east. Borrer's herbarium sheet has a specimen collected near Harting by Mr Weaver. F.C.S. Roper collected it on the downs above Danny Park in 1863 and from Folkington in 1874. Thomas Hilton made many collections on the downs between Brighton and Eastbourne.

Rev F.H. Arnold noted it by the banks of the Chichester Canal in 1883, as a site away from the chalk. It persisted in a garden in Hunston, adjoining the canal, into the 1980s, the owner of the garden being the late Bernard Price, local historian and TV pundit on bygones.

The attractive flowers make this one of the best known of all British orchids. The flower spike is 15-50cm high, rising from a rosette of five to six greyish-green, strap shaped leaves. By the time that the plant is in flower in June, the leaves are often scorched at the tips and withered. There are two sheathing stem-leaves, and the bracts are leaf-like, longer than the ovary. Most spikes bear between two and seven flowers, rarely more than twelve, each pink sepal marked with three prominent green veins. The upper inner perianth segments are shorter, brownish in colour and cylindrical in shape, as the margins are rolled inwards.

The labellum is convex and three-lobed, the lateral lobes each forming a furry brown hump, while the central lobe is velvety, marked with dark brown bands and yellow at its base. The appendage at the tip of the central lobe is folded back, and not immediately apparent.

The long column is beaked and reminds me of a duck's head, while the yellow pollinia lie inside with their caudicles running down in two grooves. Soon after the flowers open the pollinia are still held within the rostellum by the sides of the grooves, and at that stage cross-pollination can occur. The caudicles quickly dry out and shrink, dragging the pollinia out of their pouches. Since they are still attached at the base, the whole mass swings forwards and downwards, to land squarely on the stigma surface. This occurs in nearly every case, so that, although apparently adapted by mimicry for cross-pollination by bees, the Bee Orchid is usually self-pollinated.

Seed is set efficiently and most spikes will bear three or more fat ripe seed capsules, each containing about 10,000 fine, dust-like seeds. Most Bee-orchids are monocarpic, flowering once and dying, but field studies by some schoolchildren in Somerset have shown that individual plants can flower for as many as eight consecutive seasons.

Traditionally the Bee Orchid is recognised as a plant of chalk and limestone, found most frequently on the downs in Sussex. Elsewhere it occurs on the gault and on outlying calcareous soils, such as the sands around Rye and Camber which contain lime from seashells. In recent years Bee Orchids have been found with increasing frequency on the verges of newly constructed roads, where calcareous or basic soils have been disturbed. It seems bizarre to see thriving colonies of Bee Orchids on round-abouts and motorway verges. They have also been recorded in beech woods, where the tree cover was not too dense.

Much has been written on the many morphological and colour forms of the Bee Orchid, resulting in a plethora of scientific names, and ranks ranging from specific to varietal. I have come to agree with D.M.T. Ettlinger that all of them should be regarded as varieties of one good species. Two varieties and a peloric form have definitely occurred in Sussex, and a further two varieties may occur in the west of the county.

Var.**chlorantha** (Hegetschweiler) K.Richter (inc.var.*flavescens* Rosbach)

Widespread but uncommon in Sussex. The flowers lack the usual red-brown pigmentation, having a green labellum and white outer perianth segments. Wolley-Dod listed an unconfirmed record for it near Eastbourne (H.Haines).

It was certainly found near Beachy Head by A.G. Gregor in 1913, E.J. Bedford in 1915 and H.W. Pugsley in 1918, all the sheets being in the Natural History Museum. It still grows there, and in 1985 between two and three hundred spikes were recorded near Birling Gap. I have seen it on the Caburn (just east of Lewes) between 1967 and 1972 and on the downs near Willingdon, and it has also been seen on Heyshott Down (1981).

Var.**trollii** (Hegetschweiler) Reichenbach

This variety has rarely been recorded in Sussex, with two old records at Upper Beeding (Henry Salt) and near Southwick in 1913 (Miss Cottis). There is a record for June 1924 from Uppark in the Reynolds herbarium in Portsmouth Museum. It is better known in Gloucestershire, Dorset and Warwickshire. More recently it was found in June 1952 by Patrick Coulcher near Folkington.

It is a curious and distinct variety, with a long pointed labellum barred with brown and yellow, lacking the U-shaped orange-yellow patch. The appendage, which is normally tucked under the convex labellum, sticks out like a sting. Forms with the pointed labellum but possessing the U-shaped patch have been wrongly recorded as var.*trollii*.

Peloric form (F.Horsman (1990) type b. peloria)

This peloric form is a Sussex speciality, having no other recorded sites in the British Isles. The labellum is replaced by a pink, sepal-like structure, with no hint of a bee. It was first found on the Caburn in June 1919 by Kathleen Pickard, who took it for identification to E.J. Bedford in Lewes. Photographs taken by him at the time turned up years later in the archives of the Lewes Historical Society, and match up exactly with those that appear at the end of Wolley-Dod's Flora of Sussex, and in a short paper published by C.B. Tahourdin in the same year. Apparently the variety flourished in some numbers, certainly until 1939, there being a herbarium sheet of Bedford's dated 14.6.1939 with as many as eight spikes mounted on it.

The site was destroyed in 1940, when the tenant farmer ploughed the area in response to the government's demand for growing more food in the early days of World War II. Then in 1967 I found two spikes of this peloric form several hundred metres away from the original site, with two more in 1969 and four in 1971. Since then no further flowers have been seen, despite many searches.

Two other varieties have been recorded in West Sussex, but need further confirmation. Flowers close to var. *friburgensis* (Freyhold) Ruppert , have been seen on Bury Hill. This form has recently be found in Wiltshire and Somerset. The two inner upper perianth segments are replaced by two broad, pink sepaloid structures, which have hairy edges.

Var. *belgarum* D.M.T. Ettlinger, is known just over the border at Winchester, also at Twyford (Hampshire) and at Bath. It was first recorded in Britain in 1998. The labellum is well rounded, with no side lobes and hairy edges. The colour is dark chestnut, with a clear-cut yellow band across the middle and several yellow subsidiary bands.

Given the manner in which the flowers of the Bee Orchid are normally pollinated, it is not surprising that hybridisation is a rare event. The hybrid with the Fly Orchid *Ophrys* x *pietzschii* Kümpel (*Ophrys apifera* Huds. x *Ophrys insectifera* L.) was first produced artificially in the wild at

Halle in East Germany in 1962. Karl Pietzsch used the pollinia of the Fly Orchid to fertilise the Bee Orchid. Three plants flowered in 1967, but eventually disappeared. The first known natural hybrid was found in Leigh Woods near Bristol in 1968. It flowered for a number of years, before it in turn disappeared. Until now that had been the only known natural population in Europe. During a routine survey of a nature reserve in West Sussex in June 1998, Sue Perry noticed an odd looking Fly Orchid, and drew it to the attention of Bruce Middleton. They sought further opinions as to what it might be. There was general agreement that this was indeed the hybrid *Ophrys* x *pietszchii*. Comparison with photographs of the Leigh Woods plants confirmed the second natural occurrence of this hybrid in Europe, and the first in Sussex. It has since flowered in 1999 and 2000.

A photograph taken by Guermonprez at East Dean, and published by C.B. Tahourdin in November 1922, shows a bunch of flowers including Fly Orchids, a Greater Butterfly-orchid and what was said to be the hybrid *Ophrys apifera* x *Ophrys sphegodes*. It appears to me to be a form of the Early Spider-orchid, *Ophrys sphegodes* var.*lutea*.

Another photograph taken by E.J.Bedford, and noted in 1926 by Tahourdin, is of the hybrid *Ophrys apifera* x *Ophrys fuciflora* (Late Spider-orchid). This was probably taken in Kent.

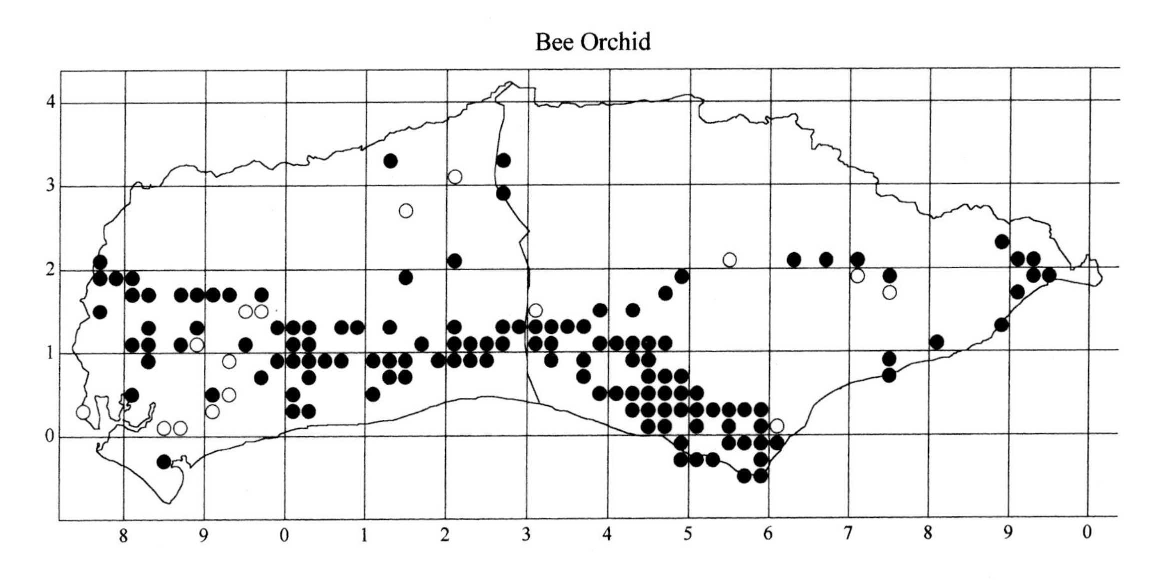

21 EARLY SPIDER-ORCHID

Ophrys sphegodes Miller
[*Ophrys aranifera* Hudson]

The Early Spider-orchid is one of my favourites, coming as it does so early in the orchid season, giving a promise of summer delights still to come.

The first record in Sussex is for 1834, and the earliest herbarium specimen I could find was for H.C. Watson in the Kew collection, found at Birling Gap on 10th May 1837. There is no doubt that the range of the species in Sussex was never great, from Pyecombe in the west to Beachy Head in the east, but in recent years it has contracted to two main centres at the Castle Hill national nature reserve near Brighton and the general area of Beachy Head.

Watson knew the Early Spider-orchid at Pyecombe in 1859, and in 1864 J. Edwards collected it there for F.C.S. Roper's herbarium. It persisted, despite many collections, until 1938, when both Dr Ursula Smith and Jim Driver found it in flower.

Roper also records it as early as 1873 from Cow Gap near Beachy Head, where many botanists went to view it, including Ted Lousley in 1936. It still flowers there despite repeated cliff falls, which in 2000 resulted in some flowering plants with their tubers exposed over a fairly substantial drop. Certainly not a place to indulge in plant photography.

Ted Lousley found a single plant at Camber Sands in May 1932 – a specimen is in Reading University herbarium – but it has never reappeared. There is still a small colony not far away at Dungeness. It was also recorded near Lewes in 1873 (Arnold's herbarium) and near Alfriston until 1968. There are also old records for Wolstonbury Hill (1946), not so far from Pyecombe, and from Piddinghoe (1960s), but it has not been seen in any of these sites for many years. It has been known on Lullington Heath, and a small group persists at a site on the edge of Brighton.

There is one very odd herbarium sheet dated May 21, 1907 from Miss C. Bray, which has three spikes from Beachy Head, but also three from 'Hailsham', which seems most unlikely.

Apart from the area between Seaford and Beachy Head, which holds more than twelve populations, the largest population is at Castle Hill national nature reserve, where Dr Mike

Hutchings of Sussex University has made a detailed study over many years. Despite problems of management in the 1970s, the site is now flourishing, with a gratifyingly large and healthy population of Early Spider-orchids, a tribute to good management in striking the right balance of grazing pressure which the downland requires.

The Early Spider-orchid is a small plant, rarely exceeding 20cm in height, frequently growing to barely 5cm in exposed turf. There are three to four bluish-green leaves in a loose rosette, with a further two or three clasping stem leaves. The bracts are leafy, long and erect.

The outer perianth segments are large, pointed-oblong and yellow green with wavy margins, the upper segment arching over the column. The upper inner perianth segments are erect, strap-shaped and often tinged orange-brown on the margins. The labellum is large and covered in velvety brown fur, with a furry hump on either side at the base, and a prominent shiny grey H mark in the centre. The column is stout, with the pollinia housed on each side in pouches, the thecae. These glisten with nectar, and look like a pair of eyes.

Pollination is by the male solitary bee *Andrena nigroaena*, and is described under **Sexual Reproduction**. The same species has been recorded as the pollinator in France, Crete and at Mt. Gargano in Italy. Seed set is poor in Sussex, only 6-18 per cent of the flowering population.

The Castle Hill population of Early Spider-orchid has been shown by Dr. Hutchings to have a much shorter life cycle than had been thought previously, most recruitment from seed being on a three year cycle. This explains why the grazing regime must be so carefully controlled. Winter grazing produces a suitable environment, but plants must be protected in early summer until they have flowered and dispersed their seed. Some of the Kent populations, in contrast, seem to behave differently, individuals being long-lived and flowering in successive years. Pollination by pseudo-copulating solitary bees in Kent is hugely successful, with almost 100 per cent of the florets developing capsules in some years.

The male solitary bee *Andrena nigroaena* pollinates the Early Spider-Orchid.

Early Spider-orchid is restricted to the short turf of old downland and calcareous pastures, with two small populations on lawns near Beachy Head.

I have found one colour form consistently in the Beachy Head colonies. This lacks the anthocyanin pigmentation, so the whole labellum is pale sage green in colour, rather smooth in texture, with the H mark indistinct and green. It is easy to confuse this form with faded individuals of the normal type, but it is obviously crisp and fresh when examined closely. It has been provisionally called var.*lutea*, but I cannot find the authority for this name.

Left: **The form of the Early Spider-orchid which has provisionally been called var.*lutea*.**

Changes in downland management could see the Early Spider-orchid re-establishing itself. In Kent there has been an extraordinary flourishing on the spoil dumped from the Channel Tunnel excavations. One plant flowered in Wiltshire in 1986, and similarly a single plant appeared on the Isle of Wight in 1992, while at Lakenheath in Suffolk it re-appeared in 1991 for the first time in the county since 1793.

Tahourdin photographed the hybrid with the Fly Orchid (*Ophrys insectifera*) in 1927, but it is not clear where the plant was found, and it might not have been in Sussex.

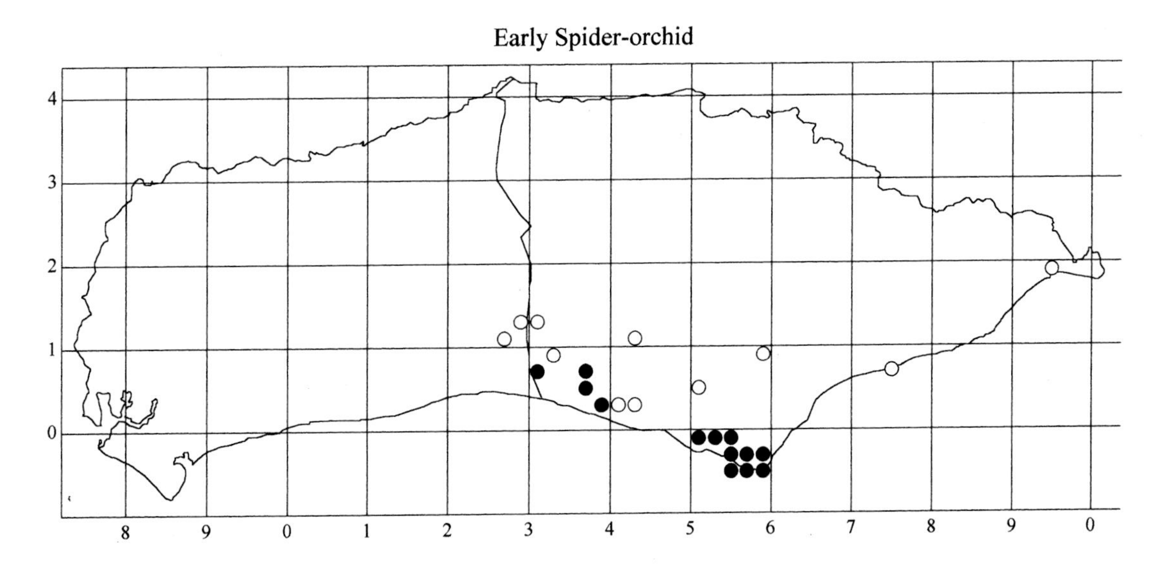

22 FLY ORCHID

Ophrys insectifera L.
[*Orchis muscifera* Hudson]

Wolley-Dod notes the first record as 1746 Orchis Myodes flore grandiusculo found by a Mr Hill in Charlton Forest. The Fly Orchid has never been common or widespread in Sussex, and has certainly decreased since Borrer's time, but it is still well distributed in West Sussex in woods on the chalk and in the western part of East Sussex.

F.C.S. Roper collected it many times, from Wolstonbury in 1862, Beeding in 1865, Glynde in 1876 and Offham in 1877. In the latter two locations it still hangs on, if a trifle precariously, to this day.

Arnold, Wolley-Dod and Guermonprez all list numerous sites in West Sussex in woods on the downs, with a fine painting by Guermonprez of flowers from Lavant in 1904 and a depressing sheet of no fewer than eight Fly Orchids in H.J. Roffey's herbarium in the Natural History Museum from the downs above Offham. It certainly has suffered from collection, and Frank Penfold remembers an elderly lady in Burpham village who took pride in collecting a good bunch of Fly Orchids from a nearby wood every spring in the 1950s and 1960s. Now there are none.

The Fly Orchid is tall and slender, and so often grows in the dark parts of woods that it is difficult to see, and is easily overlooked. The underground, egg-shaped tubers and fleshy roots

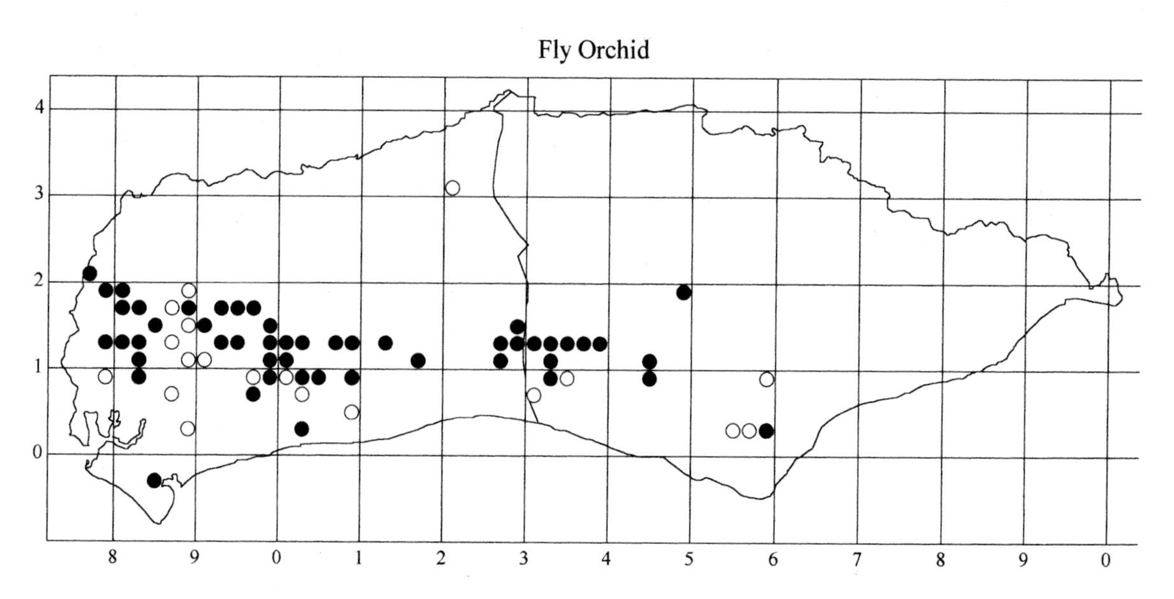

give rise to the slender stem, 15-60cm tall. The three narrow lower leaves are dark green, shiny and floppy, with an erect stem leaf above them. The bracts are long and leafy, exceeding the slender, erect ovary.

The flowers are usually well spaced on the spike, and number two to ten, rarely as many as twenty. The outer perianth segments are all pale yellow-green, pointed and stiff. The upper inner perianth segments are wire-like and purplish brown, looking just like a pair of antennae.

The labellum is long and three-lobed, the central lobe forked at the tip. It is a rich, velvety brown with a brilliant blue iridescent band across the middle. At the base of the labellum are two glistening patches which secrete nectar. They lie at the base of the 'antennae' and resemble eyes, so that the flower really does resemble an insect with folded wings.

Pollination is effected by male digger wasps *Argogorytes mystaceus*, and was first observed by M.J. Godfery in 1929. The male wasps are fooled by pheromones and attempt to copulate with the flower, in the process removing the pollinia. The female wasps emerge some days later than the males, but once the females are on the wing the males realise the error of their ways and leave the orchids alone.

In May 1981 in Wiltshire (*see following page*) Howard Jones photographed the digger wasp in the act of pseudo-copulating on a Fly Orchid flower. The photographs are quite extraordinarily beautiful, with colour and detail of an exceptional quality.

I have also seen red ants removing portions of the pollinia, probably as food for their larvae, but there is no evidence that this leads to pollination. Despite all this activity seed set is rather poor, with less than 20 per cent of capsules ripening.

Germination is rapid, with the first leaf appearing in the following winter and the first tuber in the next year.

The Fly Orchid is well distributed in woods on the chalk in West Sussex, especially in the beech 'hangers' on the north face of the downs, and also on open downland as at Heyshott Down. In East Sussex it still grows around Pyecombe, Ditchling and Stanmer Park, but it is scarce and decreasing elsewhere. It is a plant of copse and woodland, tolerating deep shade, growing even in bare soil or poking up through a carpet of Dog's Mercury. It flowers from mid-May to the end of June.

The rare hybrid with the Bee Orchid (*Ophrys* x *pietzschii*) has been described under that species.

A pale yellow, lutistic form is known in Wiltshire, and peloric forms with all three inner perianth segments replaced by a fly-like structure are known, but not in Sussex.

This stunning photograph of a digger wasp 'mating' with a Fly Orchid was taken by Howard Jones.

23 LIZARD ORCHID

Himantoglossum hircinum (.L) Sprengel
[*Orchis hircina* (L.) Crantz]

The Lizard Orchid in Britain is on the edge of the northern limits of its geographical range in Europe, and it has been suggested that a species in that situation may be unusually sensitive to climatic change. In this case it appears that wet weather during the vegetative growing period is more important than warmth.

Most early British records prior to 1910 are in south-east England, clustered around Dartford (1641), but during the period from 1910 to 1935 the Lizard Orchid became both more numerous and widespread. This picture is certainly reflected in the Sussex records, with the first in about 1850, when Henslow found many plants at Steyning growing on chalk excavated from the new railway cutting.

Hodgson found it at Boxgrove east of Chichester in 1907, and in June of that year a plant was collected from the gardens at Goodwood, and shown at the City of London Entomological Society by Dr G.C.C. Hodgson. It certainly occurred repeatedly at Goodwood Park and racecourse from 1915, when a single plant was found by Rev Arnold's daughter. It flowered at Halnaker chalkpit from 1918 to 1926, when several plants were moved to the gardens at Goodwood. A painting of a plant at Halnaker,done by Guermonprez in July 1924, is in the Portsmouth museum. It flowered at Slindon in 1924, Funtington in 1927 and as late as 1948 in Arundel Park, when a Mr Stedman picked one and gave it to Ceres Esplan.

In East Sussex it was found by E.J. Bedford in June 1911 on the downs near Jevington. It was recorded from Malling Hill in 1911, by Rev A.A. Evans at Easdon near Polegate in June 1914, and for many years it flowered in a chalkpit near Glynde, where Kathleen Pickard first found it in 1921. J.A. Sharpe collected it there in 1932, and A. Bale sent a specimen to F.C.S. Roper in 1938.

In June 1919 it was found on the downs above Plumpton by Miss May French, then a schoolgirl and collecting wild flowers for a village flower show. She thought it was a butterfly-orchid until it opened, and she sent the flower to the British Museum, where it is still preserved in the herbarium. It flowered again in 1920, 1921 and 1923. Jim Driver remembers telling E.J. Bedford about it in 1920, when he took a number of photographs, the prints of which still exist. One can see from matching details that he used them as the basis for his watercolour of Lizard Orchid in the postcard series for the Natural History Museum. Other records from Ringmer, Offham and East Dean all fall during this flourishing period, after which it was hard to find. J.E. Lousley in 1969 aptly commented that it was 'the most capricious species of them all'. The next firm record is for 1967 at Rye, where two plants flowered in 1967 and ten in 1968. It has persisted there, flowering annually, the population fluctuating in numbers, with as many as 44 in 1978. The site is carefully monitored, but cannot compare with a site on the dunes of Sandwich golf course in east Kent, where in recent years in excess of 3,000 flowering plants have been recorded.

The Lizard Orchid turned up recently in the middle of Lewes. A single plant flowered in 1985, 1986 and again in 1995, when there were 60 flowers on the spike. This was hand-pollinated, but seed set was poor, a situation also reported in Kent despite the larger population there.

During preparation of this book a single flowering plant was found in July 2000 near Amberley by Simon Mockford, the first West Sussex record since 1948.

The Lizard Orchid is a large plant, with a stout stem 25-70cm high, arising from two large ovoid tubers. The leaves are large, oblong and greyish-green, sometimes spotted with purple. They are formed in the autumn, the plant being wintergreen, but shrivel just before or during the flowering period from June to late July. The basal leaves form a loose rosette, with another three to five clasping stem leaves. The bracts are short.

The flower spike is massive, carrying up to eighty flowers. The sepals and petals are short, rounded and grey-green, forming a tight helmet marked on the inside with a series of parallel lines formed of brown dots and dashes. The labellum is an extraordinary structure, starting life tightly curled like a watch spring. As the flower opens it unfurls, at the same time twisting anti-clockwise to reveal side lobes which are long, brown and crinkled. The central lobe is brown with a white base, marked with bright crimson dots, and there is a short, rounded spur. The whole structure looks like the tail and hind legs of a little lizard – hence the name.

The other remarkable feature of the Lizard Orchid is the scent: a pungent smell of billygoat. It is difficult to know quite what advantage this may confer! Pollination has been observed to be carried out by the female Tawny Mining Bee (*Andrena fulva*) and by the Wall-mason Wasp (*Odynerus parietum*). Other insects including flies may be involved, but in any event pollination

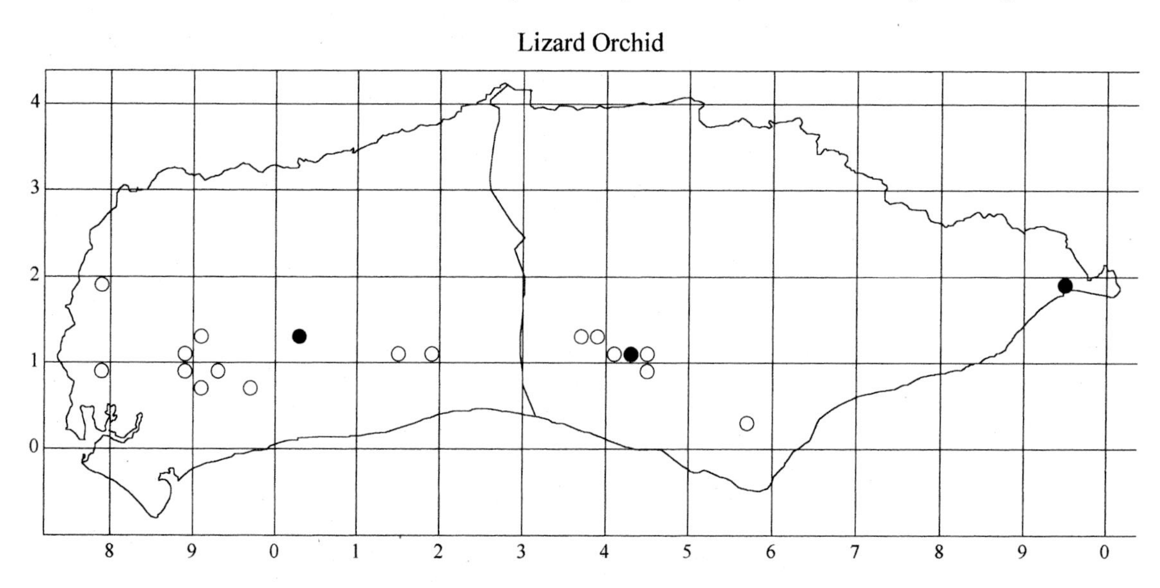

success would appear to be poor, not exceeding 20 per cent. In Gueromonprez's painting of the Lizard Orchid he depicts *Andrena fulva* in the act of pollinating a flower.

Seeds take about six weeks to ripen, and plants mature in about five years. They can be long-lived, in excess of 13 years, but may not flower in successive years even when mature. They are also capable of remaining for years as an underground tuber. The plants cannot tolerate a long drought, which leads to extensive death of seedlings and even of mature plants.

In Britain there are currently sixteen populations, of which six are on golf courses. Carey, in his article in Watsonia (1999), discusses whether golf courses just happen to supply suitable habitat, or whether golf shoes and trolleys are active agents in dispersing the species. Several new populations were reported in Kent in 1998-2000, possibly in response to global warming and milder, wetter winters. Perhaps we shall see another increase like that which occurred in the 1920s.

24 LADY ORCHID

Orchis purpurea Hudson
[*Orchis fusca* Jacques]

The Lady Orchid has traditionally been regarded as a Kentish species, with occasional records in Surrey and recently in Oxfordshire (1986) and the Avon Gorge (1990). In Sussex it has always been a plant of extreme rarity, seldom persisting even where it has been found for more than a few years.

The first record was made by Rev E.G. Smith in West Sussex at a site I cannot clearly identify. Merrifield then reports it, in the proceedings of the Natural History Society of Brighton, as growing on the downs near Pyecombe in1860. S. Evershed made the next discovery at High Down Hill near Durrington in 1886.

In 1905 it was found on the skirts of a wood near Eartham, Chichester, by a Mr J. Stallard of Bognor (*not* Dr Stallard of Eastbourne), the single specimen being perserved in Rev Arnold's herbarium. In 1911 another lone plant was found by Herbert Jenner near Lewes, as noted by J.H.A. Jenner, there being no previous record for East Sussex.

In 1935 it was said to have been found on the downs near Arundel by Mr Collier, but I can find no firm evidence for this. There is an unconfirmed record, however, for 1944 or 1945 near the edge of an unofficial car park at Goodwood, which was passed on to me by Bill Havers of the Military Orchid Project.

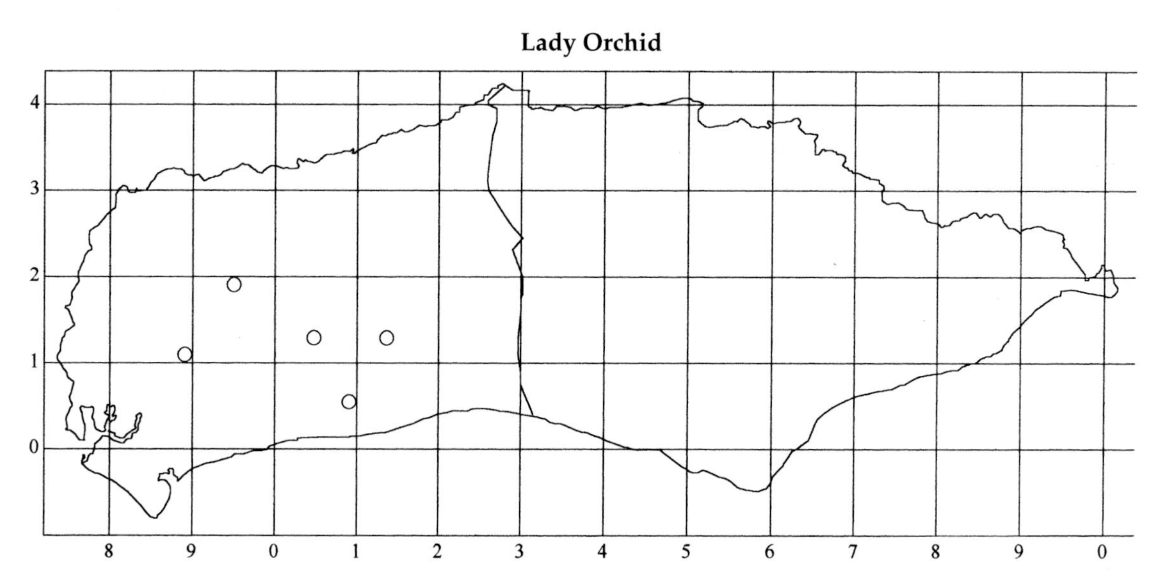

It certainly grew for a number of years near Chanctonbury, and was known there from 1947. In 1949 B.T. Lowne found only one in flower, Dr Francis Rose recorded it in 1953, Frank Penfold was shown a non-flowering plant in 1956 and Oliver Buckle saw it in 1959 – the last flowering date given in the Sussex Plant Atlas (1980). However, Jonathan Simons records it still there in 1976 and 1977, before it was finally destroyed by cattle in 1981. The other unconfirmed record is for a site near Rackham in 1975, but at the present time I know of no Lady Orchids in Sussex.

Lady Orchid has two large, ovoid tubers, and a stout stem 20-100cm high. There are three to five broad, oval, pointed tipped leaves, dark green and shiny, which form a loose rosette, and several narrow, sheathing stem leaves. The bracts are very small, reduced to violet coloured scales. The robust flower spike may have as many as fifty large flowers, each of which looks remarkably like a little lady in a bonnet, wearing a crinoline.

The outer periant segments are connivent, dark reddish-brown, and completely hide the two upper inner segments, which are strap-shaped. The labellum is broad and flat with two long lateral lobes which form the lady's arms, and a broad central lobe which is sub-divided into two round lobes and may have a small tooth in the notch of the division. The labellum is white or pale pink, with a cluster of crimson spots, each formed by a tiny papilla crowned with bunches of coloured hairs. The spur is pale pink and less than half the length of the ovary. The colour of the labellum may on occasion be pure white, without spots, or heavily pink-flushed with dark purple spots. The colour of the hood will similarly range from a pale straw colour to dark reddish-brown.

Pollination by small digger wasps (*Odynerus parietum*) was first recorded by M.J. Godfery in 1933 and in France bees have been noted as pollinators. The percentage of ripe seed capsules is low, from 3-10per cent, and plants take eight to ten years to reach flowering maturity. They are very susceptible to being eaten off by rabbits, and in recent years by the expanding deer population, but the 'grazing' which has decimated some of the Kentish colonies appears to be due to attack by slugs.

The Lady Orchid is a plant of well-lit woodland and coppice on chalk, just occasionally flowering on open downland. It flowers from early May to mid June. It is still widespread in Kent, with more than 100 colonies, and is common on the chalk just across the Channel in the Pas de Calais and Normandy southwards into central and southern France.

Peloric forms with all the inner perianth segments forming 'ladies' have been recorded in Kent, but not in Sussex.

The hybrid between the Lady Orchid and Man Orchid (*Aceras anthropophorum*) was recorded in Kent in 1998 but, given the rarity of the happy couple in Sussex, it is very unlikely ever to be seen here.

25 BURNT ORCHID

Orchis ustulata L.

The first record is from the downs near Eastbourne in 1786, and the first specimen is in Borrer's herbarium, gathered for him at Jevington in 1805 from a site where it still grows.

Arnold's Flora lists many collections for the mid-19th century such as W.C. Unwin from Cliffe Hill, Lewes in 1850. At the Natural History Museum there is a herbarium specimen from 1849 collected near Eastbourne by E.M. Jones, while F.C.S. Roper, J.H.A. Jenner, A.G. Gregor and Thomas Hilton all collected it from sites between Portslade and Eastbourne. Wolley-Dod quotes it as abundant on the downs between Saltdean and Portobello – alas, not nowadays.

At this stage I should, like a good MP, 'declare an interest' in the Burnt Orchid. It is, without doubt, my favourite of all the British species, a diminutive and dainty version of the Lady Orchid, and an orchid which epitomises the Sussex Downs. We also have good reason to be thoroughly partisan and claim that, although there are several large colonies inWiltshire, Sussex holds the largest single consistently flowering population in Britain, .

My second reason results from many years study of the Burnt Orchid, and the opinion that it is separating into two taxa, one flowering in the third week of May and the other in July and August. By that time the early version has set seed, shrivelled up and vanished. I had thought that this behaviour was a recent development, but during research for this book I have found many herbarium sheets of this late-flowering form , which the 19th century botanists did not remark. The earliest, which is in the Natural History Museum, is for July 1849 on the downs near Eastbourne, collected by E.M. Jones. F.G. Piquet in 1874, A. Wallis and C.E. Salmon in 1906 and E.J. Bedford in 1915 all collected the late form in various sites where it still grows.

There are twelve sites for the late-flowering form in Sussex, mainly between Lewes and Eastbourne, with several more in Hampshire and Wiltshire. In Kent, strangely, only May-flowering colonies are known, while those in West Yorkshire, although the plants are often tall,

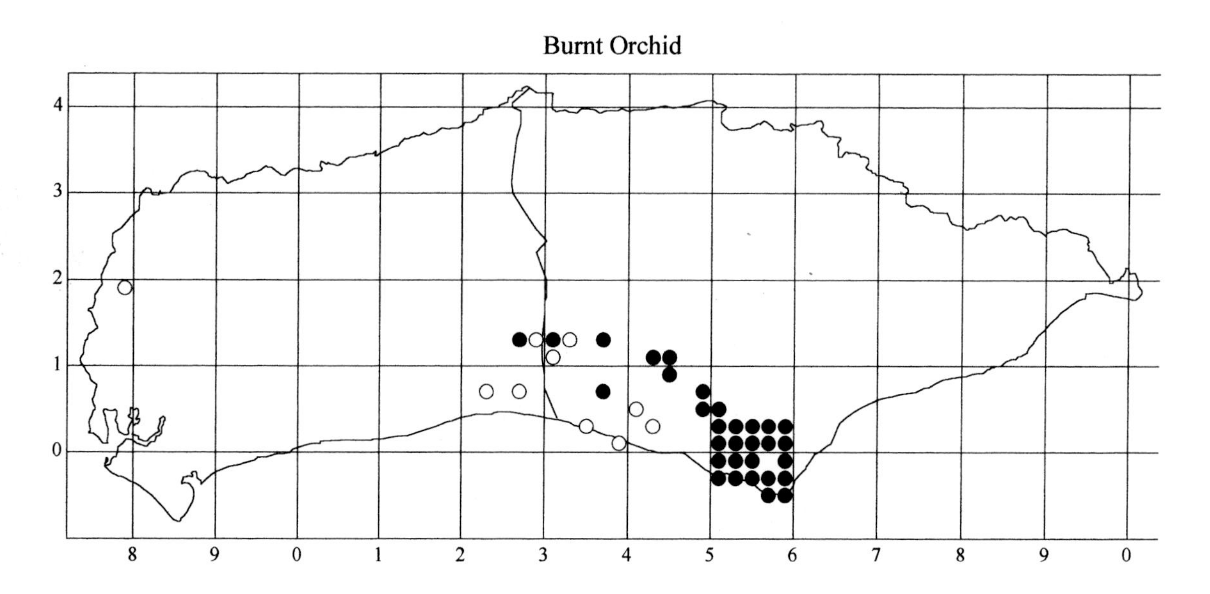

all seem to be the early taxon, both in flowering time and structure.

European botanists also find that they have two populations flowering at different times, with records of the late-flowering form from Alsace (Engel and Mathe), Fontainbleau (F Rose), Kaiserstühl (Kreutz), Estonia (K. Tali), Bulgaria (A. Petrova) and Denmark (H.A. Pedersen). They, too, separate the taxa on structural differences, but their criteria do not work in Sussex. I have found flowers exactly like the two forms they describe, but on the same plant. The plants of the Alps and Pyrenees seem to be mostly of the 'early' form, although they often flower in July because they grow at a much higher altitude.

The Burnt Orchid has two globular tubers and a stem which rarely exceeds 15cm, and is usually 6-7cm high. There is a rosette of two to five broad, channelled leaves with prominent veins, and several sheathing stem leaves. The bracts are reddish, pointed and about half the length of the ovary.

The flower spike is dense and cylindrical. The unopened buds are reddish-brown, so that the top of the spike looks burned – hence the common name. The outer and upper inner perianth segments form a tight hood which is reddish brown, but this fades rapidly in colour as the flowers open.

The labellum is pure white, marked with bright crimson spots. There are two rounded side lobes, and the central lobe is forked near the tip. There is a short, down-curved spur. The early form flowers from mid-May to the first week of June.

The late-flowering form has a more open, lax inflorescence. The reddish-brown colour of the hood does not fade, but remains in strong contrast to the white labellum. This is more stubby, with shorter 'legs', but a deeper notch between them. The spots on the labellum are larger, but most striking is the rose-magenta flush on the edges of the labellum, which sometimes extends across the middle. Neither this feature nor the persistently dark hood are never seen in the early form. The two forms rarely co-exist on the same site.

Pollination is effected by a large fly, *Tachina magnicornis*. In Denmark pollination is said to be effected by a long-horn beetle *Leptura livida*. Since the larvae of this beetle live in decaying wood, it would seem an unlikely candidate as a pollinator on the Sussex Downs.

Seed is set in a high proportion of capsules, and would appear to be the manner in which most new plants originate. Growth from seed to maturity is very slow, and may exceed fifteen years. For this reason Burnt Orchid is slow to spread and colonise new territory, and is restricted to old, undisturbed chalk downland pastures. With one exception, most of the current Sussex sites are in the east between Lewes and Beachy Head. Most colonies are small, numbering fewer than 50 flowering plants, but one site consistently produces high numbers in excess of 2500 spikes, with a record of just over 6,000 in 1992.

The Burnt Orchid flowers in the third week of May, but there is a late-flowering form *(left)* which can be seen in July and August.

Flowering depends on weather conditions and the length of the herbage. A late cold spring will depress numbers, and if the stock grazing is not intense enough, the resultant long grass will also reduce the number of flowering plants.

No hybrids are known, and none of the unusual colour forms, such as straw-coloured flowers, have been recorded in Sussex.

26 GREEN-WINGED ORCHID

Orchis morio L.

Wolley-Dod makes a note that the Green-winged Orchid was first seen in Sussex in 1784, and it is obvious from all the old flora and herbaria that it was common in damp meadows and pastures throughout the county in the 19th century. H.C. Watson collected it at Woodmancote in 1848, JWG's herbarium at Bexhill has an 1872 collection from Bepton Down, and Thomas Hilton recorded it on Ditchling Common in 1894. Guermonprez painted some delightful specimens from Lower Rucking in 1887 and Halnaker Hill in 1911, and it is clear that until the second world war there were healthy populations throughout Sussex. After that time, draining work and ploughing destroyed many of the old damp meadows on clay, and this plant with them.

There are two rounded tubers and a stem usually 6-15cm tall, although I have seen huge plants in a damp meadow which measured 40cm. There are up to seven bluish-green basal leaves and two to three pointed stem leaves which never bear spots – unlike the leaves of the Early-purple Orchid (*Orchis mascula*). The bracts are broad, pointed and about two thirds the length of the ovary, which is strongly curved.

There are usually six to twelve well spaced flowers, the outer and two upper inner perianth segments forming a loose hood. The two lateral outer segments are marked with six to seven bold parallel lines, which are green or a dark bronze colour, and give the plant its common name. The labellum is broad and three-lobed, with the wavy-edged lateral lobes folded down. The central lobe has a pale base which is marked with purple spots. The spur is long and broad, swollen at its tip, and points upwards.

Most Green-winged Orchids are purple in colour, although that can vary from pale lilac to blackish-purple. In most large populations 0.1 per cent are pure white, with the green veins in the hood very clear to see. A smaller number may be bright pink, and once in Sussex, near Seaford, I have seen a plant with straw-coloured flowers. Unfortunately it was devoured by slugs before I could return to photograph it.

There has been much debate on the presence or absence of scent in the Green-winged Orchid. In many plants I have found a strong vanilla scent, while other botanists cannot detect it at all, or record it as faint. The suggestion has been made that pale coloured flowers are more strongly scented, or that scent may be a property of certain populations only.

Pollination has been recorded by worker bumble bees *Bombus sylvarum*. Seed is set in a good proportion of flowers. Plants can flower after three years, and they then usually die. It is virtually impossible to be sure of this in large colonies, where marking individuals is not practicable.

The Green-winged Orchid is still present across most of Sussex, despite the loss of old meadows, with small populations in churchyards, on lawns and tennis courts, with rather fewer records from the chalk downs. There are still a number of impressively large populations on private land, where they are looked after with great care, one near Chichester with an estimated 50,000 flowering plants and another on the downs near Shoreham with a population numbering in excess of 30,000 – giving the pasture a purple sheen.

The Green-winged Orchid occurs sparsely throughout England and Wales, with just one Scottish site, on the coast of Ayrshire. Sympathetic management of country churchyards can result in a remarkable recovery in the number of flowering plants, and this has certainly been the case in Sussex, with good examples at Staplefield and Barcombe.

Three colours of Green-winged Orchid. From left to right: the most common purple colour (which can itself vary from pale lilac to blackish-purple), the pink form and the white form.

One good site in East Sussex occupies the turfed roof of a water reservoir. In 1994 ground water was found to be contaminating the supply, and in order to repair the roof the turf had to be stripped. South East Water Company undertook the task with great care in the winter of 1994, all the turves being stacked on pallets ready to be replaced, only for the weather to play unfair with a severe drought. Despite every effort, the replaced turves looked very sick, but since then the colony has completely recovered its former glory and extended on to neighbouring grassland.

A common feature of many colonies of Green-winged Orchids on clay soils is the presence of Adder's-tongue (*Ophioglossum vulgatum*), a tiny, bright green fern, and cowslips in abundance.

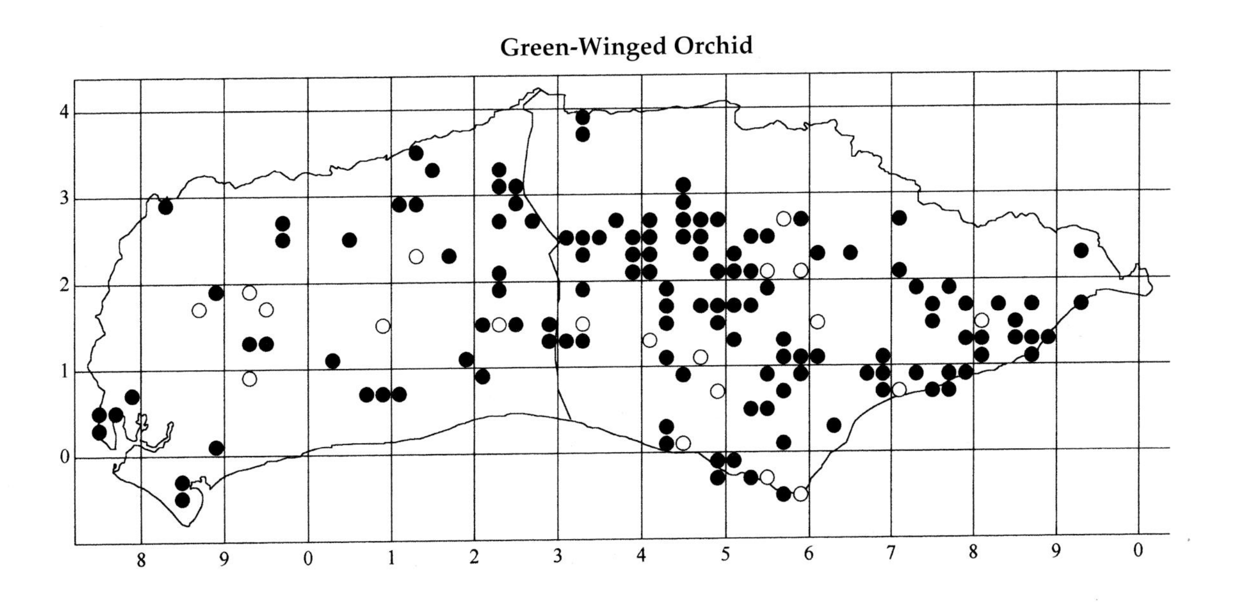

27 EARLY-PURPLE ORCHID

Orchis mascula (L.)L.

Of all the British orchids the Early-purple Orchid possesses more common names than any, including Rams-horns (Sussex), Regals (Dorset), Kettle-cases (Isle-of-Wight), Cuckoo-flower (Devon), Gethsemane (Cheshire) – probably named for the blood-like spots on the leaves – and the delightful Granfer Griggles, also from Dorset (per Roy Vickery).

V.S. Summerhayes found a reference to Early-purple Orchid in Shakespeare's *Hamlet*, where the Queen, speaking of the deranged Ophelia, says:

> *There with fantastic garlands did she come*
> *Of crow-flowers, nettles, daisies, and long purples:*
> *That liberal shepherds give a grosser name,*
> *But our cold maids do dead men's fingers call them.*

The 'long purples' refer to the flower spike, and the shepherds were clearly referring to the two round tubers!

The first Sussex reference is in 1768, and the first record comes from Chichester in the same year. All the old floras refer to the Early-purple Orchid as being very common in woods and meadows, and happily that situation continues.

It is quite a stout plant with a stem 15-60cm high and a rosette of four to eight blunt, shiny leaves, which are usually, but not always, marked with large, elongated purple blotches. There are several pointed stem leaves and long bracts which equal the ovary.

The flower spike is lax, with twenty to as many as fifty reddish-purple flowers. Woodland forms tend to be taller and more spindly, while plants on the open downs can be quite dumpy. The purple lateral outer perianth segments are at first spreading, but then fold right back like a pair of wings. The upper segment and two upper inner segments form a loose hood.

The labellum is three-lobed, the two lateral lobes folded down, and the longer central lobe

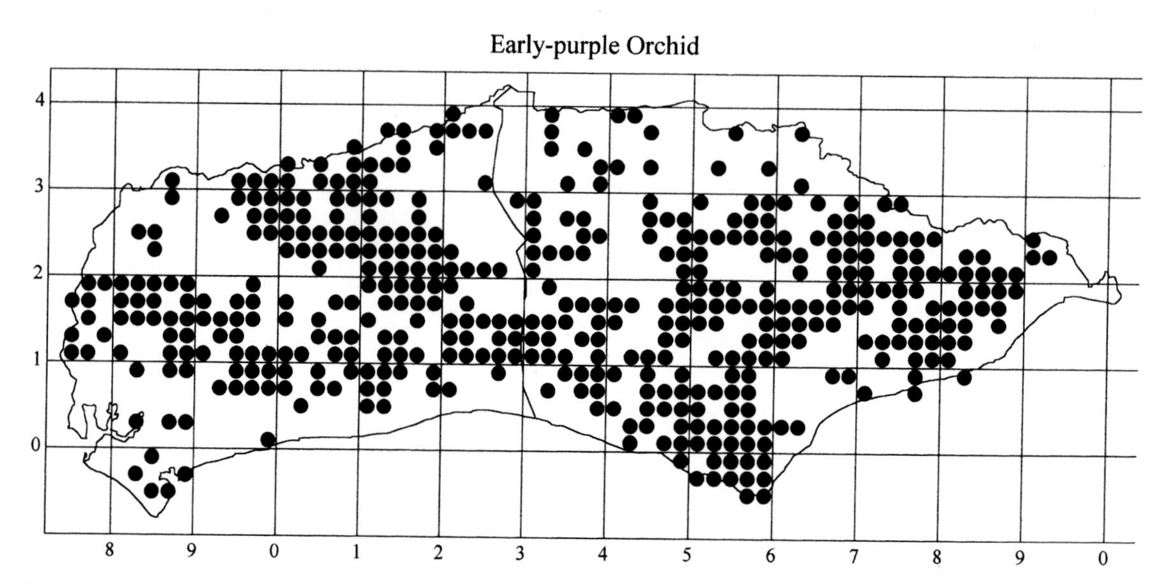

notched at the tip. The edges of all the lobes are crenated. The centre of the labellum is pale yellow or white, spotted with crimson, and the spur is long, stout and upcurved.

A form with a grossly inflated spur was found on the downs near Steyning in 1983. Plants with white flowers are not uncommon, such plants usually having unspotted leaves.

There is a most unusual colour form where the flowers are pale but flecked with purple, and the leaves are unspotted. It is very unusual to find 'broken' colour in orchids. This form has been found at Broadchalke in Wiltshire (1989) and north of Charing in Kent (1991). It should be looked for in Sussex.

The scent of the Early-purple Orchid, like that of the Green-winged Orchid, is a cause of argument. When the flowers first open many observers find the scent sweet, almost like that of honey, for which I have reports from as far

afield as Ashdown Forest (Madeleine Reader), Acharacle in West Argyll (Lynne Watson) and Sweden (Kalle Sahlin). Others say that it stinks of tomcat's urine, and I know of at least one instance where a child has picked a bunch of Early-purple Orchids for Mummy, who has promptly pushed the cat outside and prowled the house with a damp floor-cloth! Collins (1971) in Scented Wildflowers of Britain makes the suggestion that the scent changes from sweet to foul after fertilisation has occurred, and it seems that the transformation acts as a device to warn off potential pollinating insects from flowers which have lost their attraction.

Pollination is effected by workers of the Buff-tailed Bumble Bee (*Bombus terrestris*), with a high proportion of plants setting seed. It develops more slowly than the Green-winged Orchid, taking more than five years to flower, after which most plants die. It can remain in a vegetative state for years, flowering when woodland is cleared and the light increases. At a site near Lewes I could always find a dozen flowers on the edge of one particular wood, but the year after scrub clearance beside the wood the flower spikes could be counted in thousands.

The Early-purple Orchid deserves its name and is often the first orchid to flower in the spring. I saw it in full flower on April 13, 1966, poking its heads out of a mass of newly fallen snow. It will continue in flower until mid-June.

Early-purple Orchid is widespread and common across the whole of Sussex, in woods and copses, on road verges and on the open downs. It is frequent throughout Britain.

Apart from the odd colour forms already mentioned, I found an abnormal plant at the foot of Beachy Head in 1967 with 17 massive basal leaves and a fasciated stem 40cm high with hundreds of flowers.

White form of the Early-purple orchid.

28 COMMON SPOTTED-ORCHID

Dactylorhiza fuchsii (Druce) Soó
[Orchis fuchsii Druce
Orchis maculata auct.*meyeri* Reichenbach]

There are two spotted-orchid species and six marsh-orchid species in Britain, all belonging to a group known as Dactylorchids, from the generic name *Dactylorhiza* – literally 'finger rooted' – since the palmately lobed tubers bear some resemblance to a hand with fingers. They are not easy to separate, and since they also hybridise freely the picture is complex and difficult for the beginner to disentangle. Fortunately for the botanist in Sussex we have only the two spotted-orchids and two of the marsh-orchids to contend with.

One problem we do have with the early records such as those of Arnold (1887) is that the two spotted-orchids were

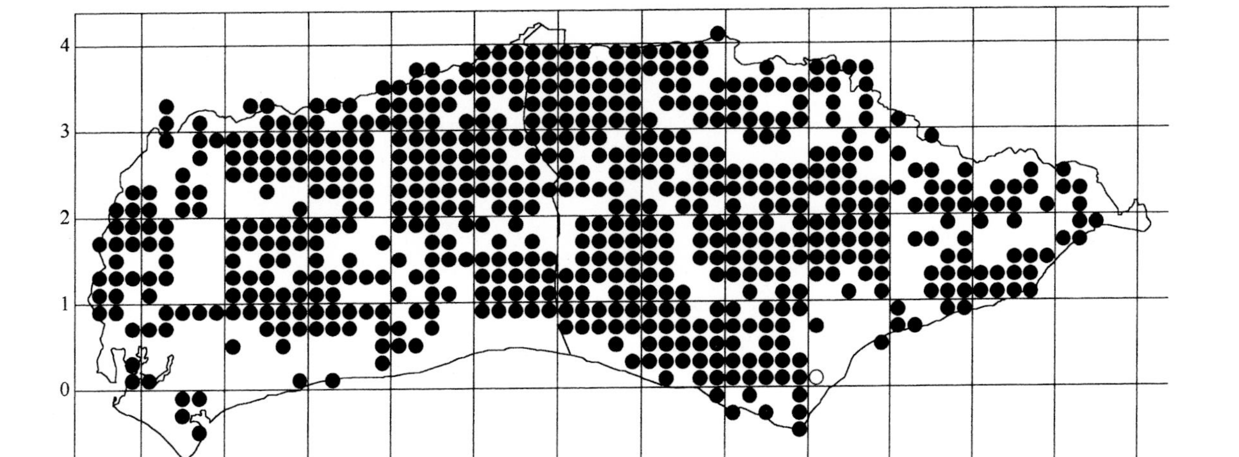

not recognised as separate species at that time: even in the Flora of Sussex (1937) such divisions as were made are not now recognised.

There is one characteristic difference between the spotted and marsh orchids which, in my experience, is consistent and serves to separate them readily in the field. The spur of the spotted-orchids is thin and parallel sided, while that of the marsh-orchids is fat and conical. In F1 hybrids between the two groups the fat spur of the marsh-orchids proves dominant – but beware hybrid swarms where introgression may dilute this feature.

The Common Spotted-orchid tubers are divided into four or five tapering lobes, with a few shallow-set fleshy roots above them. The stem is 15-45cm high, with numerous narrow, pointed basal leaves and three to five clasping stem leaves which grade into the lower bracts. The leaves are usually spotted or blotched, there being enormous variety in the markings. Some leaves may be plain, others bear a few small spots, while yet others are almost covered in big purplish brown, laterally elongated blotches. The bracts are pointed and longer than the ovary.

Above: the normal form of the Common Spotted-Orchid. Facing page: the white form (top) and var. rhodochila.

The flower spike is long and tapering, densely packed with many pale lilac-coloured flowers. The lateral outer perianth segments are spreading, marked with lines and dots, the other segments forming a loose hood.

The labellum is three-lobed, fairly deeply divided, with rhomboidal outer lobes and a triangular longer central lobe. It is well marked, with a symmetrical double loop of lines and dots. The spur is straight and slender.

White flowered plants are not uncommon, usually having unspotted leaves and yellow pollinia. It is easy to mistake faintly marked flowers for albinos.

The other abnormal colour form is striking. The leaves are sometimes entirely plain but bronze-coloured, while the labellum has a solid vertical zone of dark reddish-purple. It has tentatively been named *Dactylorhiza fuchsii* var.*rhodochila* by D.M.T. Ettlinger in a paper published in 1991. This form does occur in Sussex, and has recently been found at Warnham near Horsham (1988), near Worthing (1993) and on Barlavington Down (1993). However, it was first found by R. Edwards south of Storrington in 1973, and there is even an old record – although obviously not recognised as var.*rhodochila* – from Patching in June 1870. This was collected by G.A. Joad, and as far as I can discover this was the first record in Britain for the form. It has been recorded recently in Surrey and Lincolnshire.

Several insects have been recorded as pollinators, syrphid flies, the female Cuckoo Bee *Psithyrus barbutellus*, and more recently a small brown beetle *Dascillus cervinus*. This was photographed removing pollinia at Kenley Common in Surrey in 1994 by A.N. Scott. The beetle is not uncommon on chalk downs. Recently I took photographs of a worker Buff-tailed Bumble Bee (*Bombus terrestris*) pollinating flowers near Lewes.

Successful pollination occurs in many flowers, and seed dispersal accounts for most new plants, which take five or six years to reach flowering maturity. Having done so, they are perennial for some years, with vegetative multiplication leading to the formation of clumps of plants of varying maturity and stature.

The Common Spotted-orchid flowers from mid-May to the end of July, the later date being for plants in woodland.

It is very common and widely distributed across all of Sussex, with the exception of truly acid soils, where it is replaced by the Heath Spotted-orchid. It favours sheltered sunny banks, such as those of railway cuttings and old chalk pits, and can appear in large numbers.

The Common Spotted-orchid hybridises not infrequently. The hybrid with the Southern Marsh-orchid (*Dactylorhiza praetermissa*) is well recorded in Sussex from Arundel, East Chiltington, Malling Down, Piltdown, Newhaven, Eastbourne, Friston Forest and Rye Harbour. The hybrid with the Fragrant Orchid (*Gymnadenia conopsea*) is also not uncommon, and I have seen it at Wolstonbury Hill, Ringmer, Beddingham and Alciston.

The possible hybrid with Lesser Butterfly-orchid (*Platanthera bifolia*) photographed by E.J. Bedford has been described under that species.

29 HEATH SPOTTED-ORCHID

Dactylorhiza maculata (L.) Soó ssp.*ericetorum* (E.F.Linton) Hunt & Summerhayes
[*Orchis ericetorum* (E.F.Linton) A.Bennett
Orchis elodes Grisebach
Orchis maculata L.]

As I mentioned with the previous species, Common Spotted-orchid, there is a problem with the interpretation of historical records of the spotted-orchids, since in the past no clear distinction was made. Wolley-Dod (1937) mentions the Heath Spotted-orchid as present in all his county divisions. It certainly is widespread, but occupies those areas which are mainly acidic, such as heathland, and so occurs in areas where the Common Spotted-orchid is absent.

The earliest record I can find is a herbarium specimen in the Natural History Museum, collected in August 1901 by E.S. Gregory from a heath near Graffham. With it is a collection from Chailey Common in June, 1909 by Thomas Hilton. There is one intriguing specimen which was collected by E.J. Bedford near Eastbourne, but he does not name the site, and it is not now known anywhere in that area. Guermonprez photographed Heath Spotted-orchid on Ashdown Forest in 1922, and C.B. Tahourdin used this as an illustration in one of his Orchid Notes in November, 1922.

The Heath Spotted-orchid is usually a robust plant 10-25cm tall, occasionally as much as 40cm, with a slightly ridged stem. The leaves are all narrow and pointed and are seldom as heavily spotted as those of the Common Spotted-orchid. Frequently they are unspotted. The bracts exceed the ovaries in length.

The flower spike in most plants is short, pyramidal in shape and very pale pink in colour. The lateral outer perianth segments are short, blunt and spreading, marked with faint red lines and dots. The upper outer segment and the two upper inner segments form a loose hood.

The labellum is broad and flat, almost skirt-like, with two wavy-edged broad outer lobes and a small triangular centre lobe which is often shorter than the lateral lobes. The markings on the labellum are a mixture of dots and short lines. They extend over the entire surface and do not form the double loop which is so pronounced on the labellum of the Common Spotted-orchid. The spur is very slender and shorter than the ovary.

Occasionally deeply pigmented flowers may be found. I have seen them not infrequently in the New Forest, but they are uncommon in Sussex. The flowers, faintly scented, attract a variety of insects including the male Bristly Fly (*Empis tesselata*) and a true fly *Ptychoptera contaminata*, which I have photographed pollinating flowers in an ancient meadow near Heathfield. There I also watched a rusty coloured, narrow-bodied beetle, with a red-tipped abdomen and small head, pollinating flowers, but I failed to identify it.

Seed production is good, and plants mature in a similar fashion to those of the Common Spotted-orchid, and like them can be perennial for some years on reaching maturity. There is less tendency to vegetative propagation and the formation of clumps of plants.

The Heath Spotted-orchid is far less widely distributed than its counterpart in Sussex, but can flower in profusion in old meadows on clay or on acid soils and particularly heathland, such as Ashdown Forest and the heaths of West Sussex. It flowers a week or so later than the Common Spotted-orchid, from early June to early August.

A photograph taken in June 1931 by E.J. Bedford purports to show the hybrid with Lesser Butterfly 0rchid (*Platanthera bifolia*). The site is not recorded and the photograph is not entirely convincing. Hybrids with other species are well known in many parts of Britain, but are unlikely in Sussex as the other parents do not occur.

A recent French paper by X.Grémillet (1996) on this species in North Finistere is worthy of interest. He describes three sub-species, each of which grows in specific conditions:

Ssp. *maculata* – in well-drained alkaline sites

Ssp. *ericetorum* – in recolonised sites where sand has been extracted

Ssp. *elodes* – in damp, very acid sites with boggy vegetation

We may have to re-consider the nomenclature of the Heath Spotted-orchid.

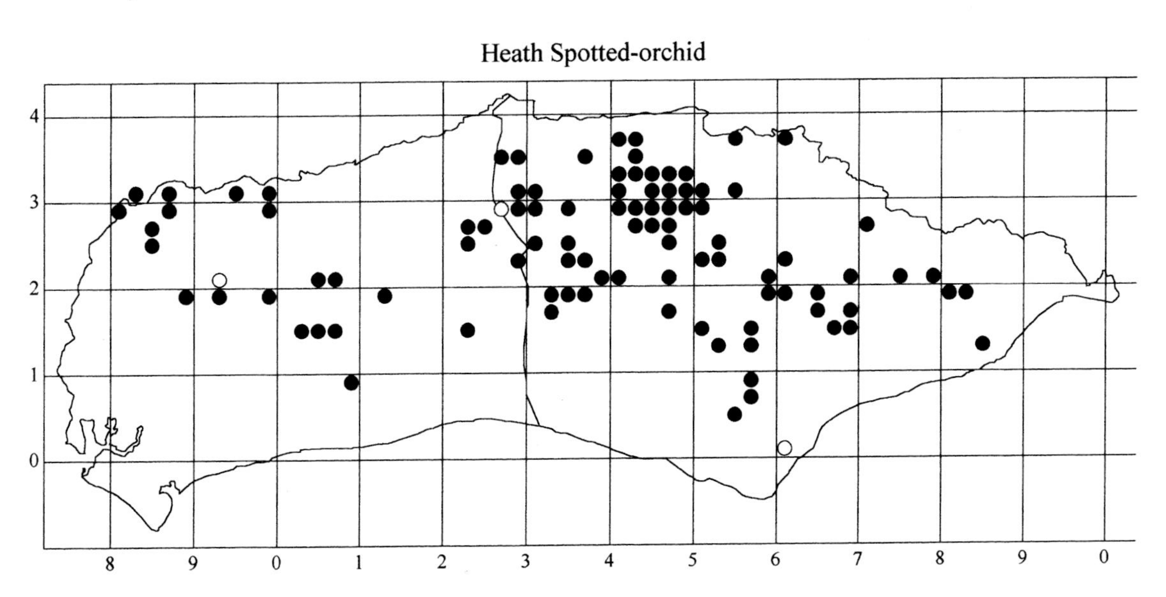

30 EARLY MARSH-ORCHID

Dactylorhiza incarnata (L.) Soó
[*Orchis latifolia* (L.) Pugsley
Orchis incarnata L.
Orchis strictifolia Opiz.]

The Early Marsh-orchid was first noted in 1843 near Chichester, with the first firm record in Arnold's Flora of Sussex as 1887 from Racton by the Ems, where it appears to have been found by W.W. Newbould. However, in F.C.S. Roper's herbarium there are several earlier records from a bog near Horsham, from Abbott's Wood in July 1875 and from a swampy area south of Heathfield station in June 1882.

Arnold has a number of records, from Aldsworth where the two subspecies ssp.*pulchella* and ssp.*ochroleuca* were recorded in addition to the normal form. Also from Aldermere near Westbourne, West Ashling, Fishbourne and a site near Eastbourne which I cannot identify. Guermonprez noted the above locations with the addition of Itchenor and West Harting.

There is an unattributable sheet in the Natural History Museum for Blackdown Brooks, Uckfield in June 1895 and another from a marsh between Winterbourne and Bognor where A.H. Maude found it in June 1917. It has always been a rare plant, even in the days of Arnold and Wolley-Dod, and nowadays with the loss of suitable wetland habitat it is even more uncommon.

The shape of the leaves and of the flowers make it fairly easy to identify the Early Marsh-orchid. The palmate tubers are divided into two to four tapering lobes, above which there are long spreading roots. The stem is hollow and 10-30cm high. There are four to seven erect, narrow pointed basal leaves, which are yellowish-green and strongly keeled, with hooded tips. The leaves of all forms found in Sussex are unspotted. The upper leaves sheath the stem, and grade into the long projecting bracts which are often tinged reddish-purple.

The dense flower spike bears twenty to thirty rather small flowers, which in the normal type are pale flesh pink in colour, hence the specific name. The lateral outer perianth segments fold right back so that they stand erect above the loose hood formed by the upper segment and the two upper inner segments. The lateral segments are marked with red loops and dots.

The shape of the labellum is diagnostic. It is shallowly three-lobed, with the side lobes folded down tightly, making the labellum appear very narrow. It bears a prominent double loop of dark red which encloses an area marked with dots and lines. The spur is short, stout and conical, as is typical of the marsh-orchids.

Two other colour forms distinct from the pale pink ssp.*incarnata* have been recorded in Sussex. Ssp.*ochroleuca* has a pale yellow colour unique among marsh-orchids, the plain coloured flowers lacking any loops or marks. There is the old record for Aldsworth as listed by Arnold, but it has never been seen anywhere in Sussex since then. It is a plant of alkaline fens.

Ssp.*pulchella* is mauve with the usual red loops and dots on the labellum. It is a plant more associated with acid soils, and is the commoner form seen in the New Forest. It was also known from Aldsworth.

Pollination of the Early Marsh-orchid by the female Red-tailed Bumble Bee (*Bombus lapidarius*) is well documented. Seed is set in a high proportion of flowers, plants reaching maturity in about seven years, persisting and flowering for some years thereafter.

It is a plant of wet-marsh and damp meadows, tolerating acid conditions but also growing in alkaline fens

Recent records for this species in Sussex are few. It was found at Rudgwick in 1950, near Chichester and in Sheffield Forest in 1970. More recently in 1985 ssp.*pulchella* was found on Ashdown Forest by Adrian Fowles during a dragonfly survey. Subsequently the forest ranger located another small colony nearby. It has flowered in most years but was absent in 2000.

In 1988 I found plants close to ssp.*pulchella* on Iping Common, and in 1989 Dr N. Sturt was shown ssp. *incarnata* at Leythorne, near Chichester, by Howard Matcham. They both shielded the precious plant from some very inquisitive calves while photographs were taken, and then

The subspecies *pulchella*, pictured left, is mauve – in marked contrast to the pale pink of *incarnata*.

stepped back – whereupon a calf eagerly consumed it! At the time they feared that they had witnessed the exinction of ssp.*incarnata* in Sussex. In 1996 I was shown both ssp.*incarnata* and ssp.*pulchella* growing in good numbers in Ferring Rife, an excellent marsh-orchid site, but one threatened by development.

In the summer of 2000 in a meadow reserve near Etchingham in East Sussex fifteen plants flowered, twelve of ssp.*incarnata* and rather surprisingly three of ssp.*pulchella*. In the autumn of 1989 the meadow was seeded with 'meadow mix for clay soils E2 and E2F' from Emorsgate Seeds, in an attempt to restore it to a status similar to other ancient meadows. The seed mixture ran short, and another locally harvested mix was used to complete the task. No orchid species were listed in either mix. Green-winged Orchid (*Orchis morio*) and Common Spotted-orchid (*Dactylorhiza fuchsii*) both appeared in good numbers in the years following, but not until 2000 did the Early Marsh-orchids appear. There are no records, past or present, for this species anywhere within a reasonable distance of the meadow, and the time interval since the original seeding – eleven years – increases the probability that the seed has arrived by natural means, possibly wind-blown over a considerable distance.

The red, sand-dune ssp.*coccinea* and the spotted leaved ssp.*cruenta* do not occur in Sussex or in any of the adjacent counties.

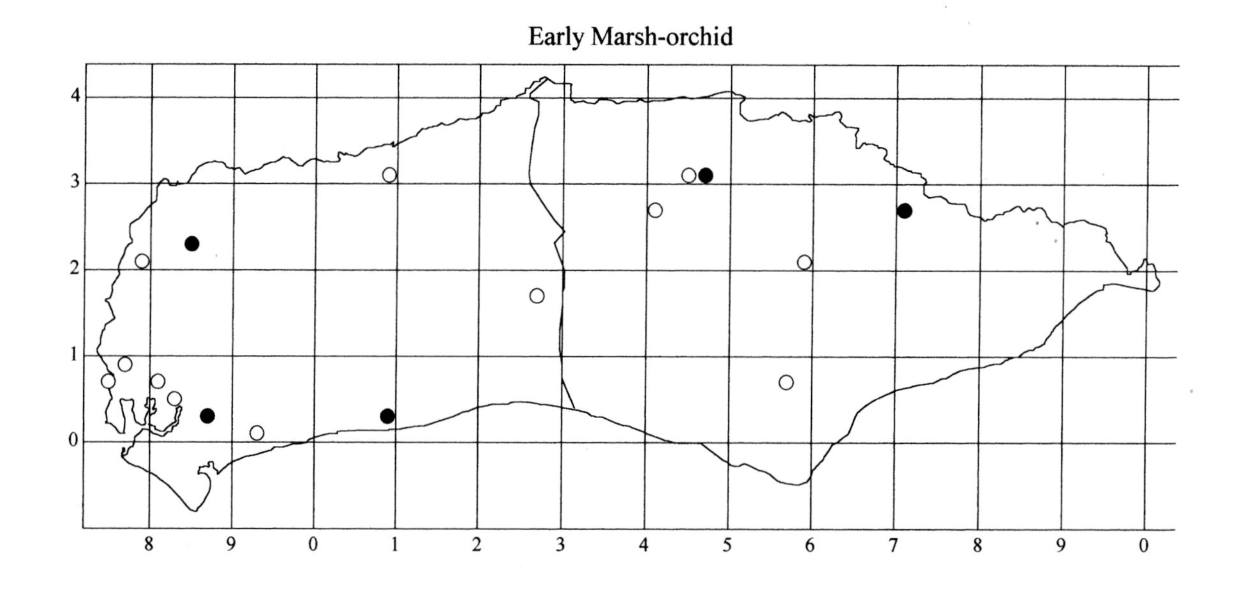

31 SOUTHERN MARSH-ORCHID

Dactylorhiza praetermissa (Druce) Soó
[*Orchis praetermissa* Druce
Orchis pardalina Pugsley
Dactylorhiza praetermissa ssp. *junialis* (Vermeulen) Soó]

The early records for Southern Marsh-orchid in Sussex remain problematical because of the difficulties with identification and taxonomy. Arnold certainly knew the species well in West Sussex and in his 1887 Flora of Sussex lists it from Petworth and Amberley as well as sites in East Sussex. One particular reference to 'Lewes levels near Iford' may be the site near Kingston which was visited many times by Thomas Hilton in 1874, A.G Gregor in 1899, R.W. Roffey in 1916 and Wolley-Dod in 1932. H.W. Pugsley visited the colony in 1933 and returned several times, obviously intrigued by the unusual forms which he found – and which still exist there. J.E. Lousley, V.S. Summerhayes and E.J Bedford all collected specimens for their herbaria there in 1939 within a few days of each other, and all comment on the variations they found.

Other colonies between Cooksbridge and Hamsey near Lewes were visited by Miss H. Salmon in 1909, and E.J. Bedford with H.W. Pugsley in 1919. They still exist today, although much reduced in numbers. Wolley-Dod (1937) lists many sites in both West and East Sussex, and despite the loss of more than twenty five of these, the picture today is nothing like as dire as that for *Dactylorhiza incarnata*.

The Southern Marsh-orchid is a robust plant with large palmate tubers and a stem that can reach 70cm. The leaves are unspotted and form a bushy cluster at the base of the stem. They are broad and flat, not hooded at the tips. The sheathing stem leaves grade into the bracts, which are often red tinged and project beyond the flowers, but not as far as in the Early Marsh-orchid.

The lateral outer perianth segments are spreading at first, but later become erect, and there is a loose hood. The labellum is broad and spreading, and can be slightly concave, with entire edges. The base is paler and often marked with red dots, but never the double loops so typical of the Early Marsh-orchid. The spur is fat and conical, sometimes slightly down-curved. The colour is variable,from pale pinkish-lilac to deep mauve with darker labellar markings.

Southern Marsh-orchid flowers from early June to the end of July. Pollinating insects have not been recorded at all thoroughly, but I have seen Large Skippers (*Ochlodes venata*) removing pollinia. Seed set is moderately good, and spread by seed seems efficient, with plants maturing in five years or so. Vegetative reproduction also occurs and clumps of flowering plants will develop. It is far less exacting in its growing requirements, flourishing in old wet meadows, on golf courses, in wetmarsh and even on the top of the downs, although it rarely persists long in such a site.

It is widely but sparsely distributed across Sussex, with recent records from Leythorne near Chichester, Sidlesham, Littlehampton golf course, Hamsey near Lewes, High Hurstwood, Uckfield, Piltdown, Chalvington, Hastings, Rye Harbour and near Cowden (but just inside the county boundary). Until 1980 it grew profusely at Marshall Road, Eastbourne, but it has now disappeared under concrete. Downland sites include the top of Heyshott Down and Malling Down near Lewes – not quite where one would expect to find a marsh-orchid.

The hybrid between Southern Marsh-orchid and Common Spotted-orchid (*Dactylorhiza fuchsii*) is not uncommon, and confusing hybrid swarms can arise, as at Cowden, which show intermediate characters with spotted leaves, three-lobed labella and stout spurs.

Some authorities also describe *Dactylorhiza praetermissa* ssp. *pardalina*. This bears ring-like spots on the leaves, giving it the common name Leopard Marsh-orchid, and characteristic double loop markings on the labellum. Dr Francis Rose feels that it is a valid type in south England and north France, where it may be the prevailing taxon. Lousley, Pugsley and Wolley-Dod all felt it existed in the Kingston, Lewes, population. A further complication may exist. Some years ago I took a Swiss Dactylorchid specialist, Dr Erich Nelson of Montreux, to Kingston, and in his opinion there existed evidence that continental *Dactylorhiza majalis* was involved in the parentage of the plants.

The marsh-orchids continue to exercise our minds and the ingenuity of the taxonomists.

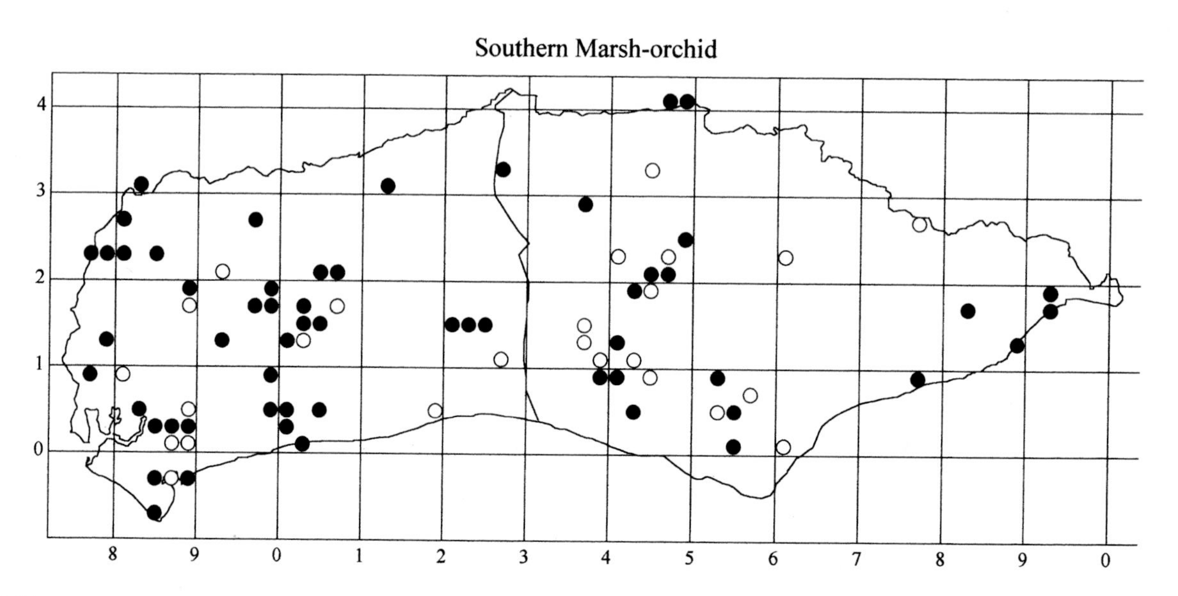

32 MAN ORCHID

Aceras anthropophorum (L.) Aitken.f.

It has always puzzled me why the Man Orchid should be so rare in Sussex, when it is not uncommon in Kent and Surrey in what appears to be the same sort of habitat.

The first record noted by Wolley-Dod is in 1832. The next was found near Barnham 'on chalky rubbish north of Westergate House' prior to 1843 by Dr Nicholas Tyacke. (He came from Cornwall, trained in Edinburgh and practised in Chichester.) The specimen is in his herbarium in Oxford.

The next record appears in Arnold's Flora of Sussex (1887). It was found 'in pastures within a seven mile radius of Horsham', (probably on paludina limestone) by George Bax Holmes and recorded in an appendix to Dorothea Hirst's History and Antiquities of Horsham (1868). Some of Holmes's records are highly unlikely, such as Early Spider-orchid (*Ophrys sphegodes*) near Horsham, so it would be wise to view the record with suspicion.

Guermonprez found the Man Orchid near Offham in 1863, as did E.J. Bedford in 1933. Both records were forgotten, and it was with some surprise and delight that it was refound in 1997, but whether in the exact same locality is unsure.

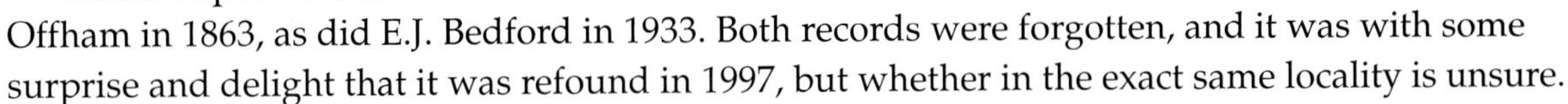

It was long known in the area between Stanmer Park and Ditchling Beacon, as noted by Mrs Merrifield in the Natural History of Brighton (1860). Jim Driver last found it there some fifty years ago. Recent searches have failed to relocate it. Mr Edwards collected it for F.C.S. Roper in 1863 from 'near Chailey', but the site is uncertain. Wolley-Dod noted that it grew on the downs towards the Cuckmere. A small colony flowered on the edge of a field near Alciston for many years, where I last saw a single flower in 1968. It was destroyed by spraying.

The furthest east it was recorded was on the shingles of the Crumbles west of Pevensey. Twenty were found in 1962, and it flowered well in 1968 (60 spikes) and 1969 (25 spikes). The flowers were extraordinarily robust and darkly coloured, but sadly the vegetated shingle ridges where it grew have all gone in the development of the new marina.

The main centre of distribution remains the area within a mile or so of Wolstonbury Hill. There are herbarium sheets collected there by Thomas Hilton in 1892 and Arnold records it as Danny Park (1887). There is a sheet in the Kew general herbarium for Wolstonbury dated July 1926, with the initials HMP. Henry Salt found it near Pyecombe in 1931.

More recently Ron Boniface recorded it in 1958. It has been found near Wolstonbury in most years since 1986, appearing erratically in six different sites, and seeming to disappear for years on end, only to pop up again unexpectedly.

There are two ovoid tubers, the current one fat and white, the older one somewhat shrivelled. The three to four blunt, bluish-green leaves are strongly veined and, rather like the leaves of the Bee Orchid (*Ophrys apifera*), the tips are frequently scorched by flowering time. The stem is stout, 15-40cm tall, although Sussex plants are rarely more than 25cm. The upper stem leaves are clasping, narrow and crowded, and the bracts are membranous, shorter than the ovaries.

The flowering spike is long and cylindrical, with as many as 90 flowers arranged in an ill-defined spiral. All the perianth segments other than the labellum are connivent in a helmet-shaped hood, the edges of the segments marked with reddish-brown. The labellum is in the shape of a hanging human figure, the two side lobes forming the arms and the forked centre lobe the legs. Occasionally there is a small median tooth between the central lobes. The colour varies from pale yellowish-green to a rich foxy-brown colour, which was so characteristic of the plants in the Crumbles population. There is no spur.

Insect pollination has not been proved satisfactorily, although red ants (*Formica fusca*) have been seen to remove pollinia, and hover-flies certainly visit the flowers for the nectar secreted in a shallow pit at the base of the labellum.

Seed is set in rather a low percentage of flowers, and the period to flowering maturity is not known for certain. Mature plants are certainly perennial for some years in my experience, but they do not flower every year and may not even be detectable above ground when not in flower.

The Man Orchid flowers from early May on the open downs to late June in sheltered sites.

Hybrids are rare. The hybrid with the Monkey Orchid (*Orchis simia*) was found in Kent in 1985 and the hybrid with the Lady Orchid (*Orchis purpurea*) in 1998, also in Kent.

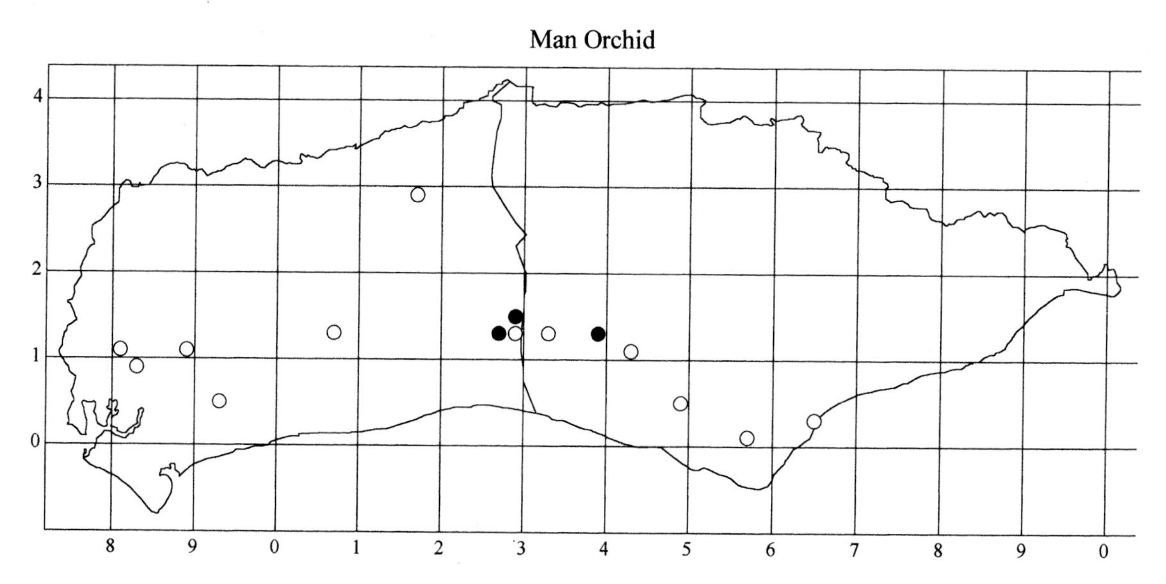

33 PYRAMIDAL ORCHID

Anacamptis pyramidalis (L.) Richard
[*Orchis pyramidalis* L.]

The earliest herbarium collection in Sussex is one by Thomas Moore from Muntham near Findon in 1849, which is at the Natural History Museum. F.C.S. Roper collected it near Clayton in July 1861, with further sheets from Ratton Woods near Willingdon in 1872 and the downs near Folkington in 1874.

All the early Sussex floras note the Pyramidal Orchid as common everywhere on the chalk, and Wolley-Dod (1937) makes a special note only of sites away from the chalk, such as Henfield, Piltdown and a field at Hackenden near East Grinstead.

The Pyramidal Orchid has two round tubers and a few slender fleshy roots. The stem is 20-60cm high. The three or four basal leaves are narrow and pointed, and being winter green are often somewhat shrivelled by flowering time. There are up to six narrow, sheathing stem leaves, and the bracts exceed the ovaries.

The flower spike is in the shape of a broad pyramid, becoming more spherical as the uppermost flowers open. It is densely packed with 50 to 100 flowers, which are usually bright pink, the colour of individual plants ranging from pale pink to red, especially in plants near the sea.

The two lateral outer perianth segments are oblong and spreading, while the upper segment and two upper inner segments form a pointed hood. The labellum is three-lobed, all the lobes being blunt and divergent. I have found enormous variability in the shape and size of the three

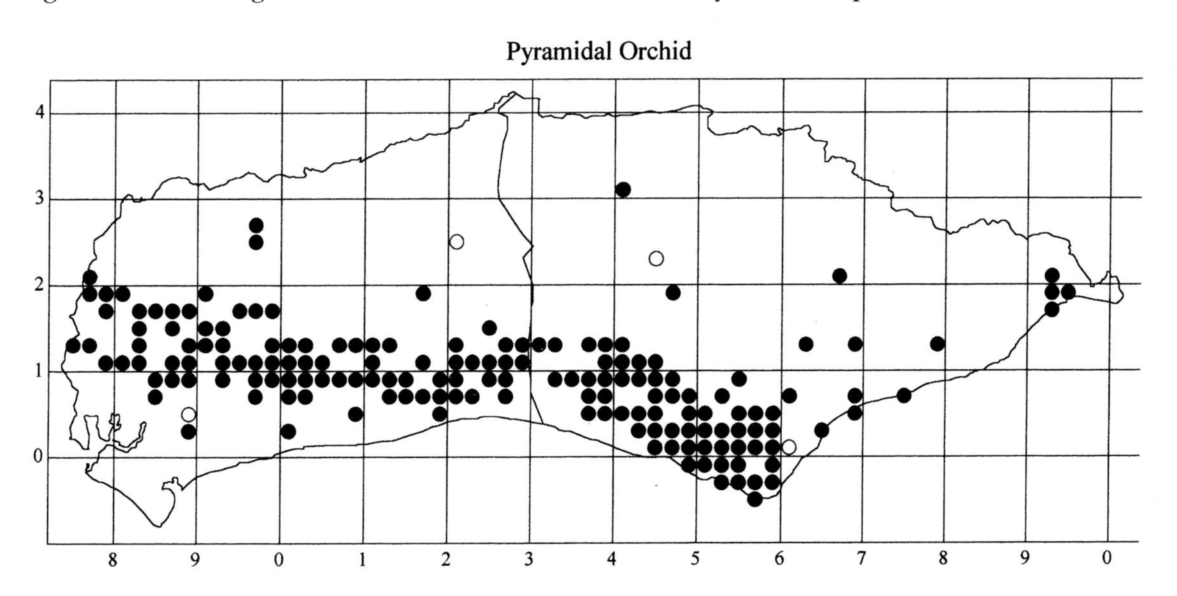

The rare form of the Pyramidal Orchid which Arthur Hoare christened *emarginata* (right) is characterised by flowers with an unlobed, entire lip. The normal form is shown above.

lobes of the labellum wherever the species occurs in Britain. At the base of the labellum are two erect plates, which angle towards the mouth of the long straight spur and act as a guide to visiting insects. The flowers are faintly scented and the spur secretes nectar.

The pollinia are prominent and linked to a single viscidium, which when detached clamps round the proboscis of the visiting insect. A burnet moth has been recorded with six sets firmly attached, which it was energetically trying to remove.

A number of insect pollinators have been recorded, including Six-spot Burnet Moth (*Zygaena filipendulae*), forester moths of the genus *Procris* and the Large Skipper (*Ochlodes venatus*). Seed set is highly efficient, as is dispersal, and plants mature in five to seven years.

Pyramidal Orchid is common in Sussex from west to east along the line of the chalk downs. There are also large populations on coastal golf courses such as Littlehampton and Shoreham, and especially on the sandy soils at Rye and Camber. Small populations occur on heaths in the west, possibly on imported lime-rich material, and at places such as road verges in the Weald, but it is primarily a chalk lover.

This is a highly successful opportunist species, rapidly establishing itself on disturbed ground which is calcareous or basic. It forms large colonies on the sides of new roads and motorways, and makes a welcome splash of colour which attracts the attention even of non-botanists.

Albinism is uncommon, but the flowers are strikingly beautiful when they do occur. In 1974 on the South Downs Arthur Hoare found a population in which about 10 per cent of flowers had an unlobed, entire lip, a form which he christened var.*emarginata*. In subsequent years the number of abnormal plants decreased and finally disappeared. In 1979 a single plant of this form was seen some thirty miles from the original site, and in 1994 I found a single specimen on Wolstonbury Hill.

In 1990 Duncan Fletcher photographed a peloric form near Burton Down in West Sussex, where the central lobe of the labellum was extended like a pointed tongue, and the two side lobes were virtually non-existent.

The Factoid File

The following five orchid species have been added to the list because they are 'factoids' (for definition see **Glossary**). They may just possibly have occurred in Sussex, or have been planted for scientific purposes and might disperse to sites nearby.

LATE SPIDER-ORCHID

Ophrys fuciflora (Crantz) Moench & Reichenbach

The Late Spider-orchid has always been a Kentish speciality, with unconfirmed very old records from Surrey, Gloucestershire, Suffolk and Dorset.

In 1974 it was reported from the downs near Edburton by a Mr James, who knew the species well in Kent. No flowering date was given, but the locality was precise. Subsequent searches have not been able to confirm the record, but in the last few years the Late Spider-orchid has flourished in Kent, and it is not unreasonable to hope that it may in time become part of the Sussex flora.

MILITARY ORCHID

Orchis militaris L.

The Military Orchid has always enjoyed notoriety as one of the rarest species occurring in Britain, having accumulated a collection of records ranging from the probable to the undoubtedly spurious.

Most records come from the chalk hills of the Chilterns, where it became progressively rarer and was thought by the late 1920s to be extinct. In 1947 the famous botanist Ted Lousley discovered a thriving colony at Homefield Wood in Buckinghamshire, but refused to divulge the locality, setting off an intensive hunt by other botanists thoroughly excited by his discovery. The locality was eventually found, and in 1956 a gleeful telegram 'The Soldiers are at home in their field' was sent to the thoroughly ruffled Lousley by Richard Fitter and Francis Rose.

For more than a hundred years a rumour persisted that the Military Orchid had been found in Kent, but no proof could be found until, in 1998, a herbarium sheet was discovered in Bolton Museum with an undoubted specimen collected in 1836 by Sir Joseph Woods from Cobham near Rochester. Woods lived in Lewes from 1833 until his death in 1864, and collected both locally in Sussex and throughout Britain. Rumour also reported the Military Orchid from 'near Goodwood' in 1924, but no more data is available.

In June 1934 Col R.S. Vine of Crowborough was on summer camp with his regiment near Eastbourne. He and his wife are said to have collected a single spike of the Military Orchid from the downland slopes above Wannock. This was 'sent to Kew for identification'. No record has been found either at Kew or at the Natural History Museum, and no herbarium sheet seems to exist, although knowing how avidly botanists of that period were seeking the Military Orchid, one can scarcely imagine it being thrown away. There are many herbarium sheets collected by Vine over some years in the orchid herbarium at Kew. They are meticulously prepared and annotated, and I cannot imagine his making a mistake. It would be exciting if the 'Bolton experience' were to be repeated.

MONKEY ORCHID

Orchis simia Lamarck

The Monkey Orchid has probably never occurred in Sussex. There is a reference in the Flora of Sussex from Petworth in 1801, as being found by a 'Mr Sokot', and featuring in F. Bauer's drawings of British orchids.

I am indebted to Dr Nick Sturt for the following details: 'The complete story about Mr Sokot is as follows. F. Bauer was shown the Monkey Orchid which he painted for the celebrated book by someone whom he called Mr Sokot with a Petworth connection. It seems highly probable that this is the Thomas Sockett (Bauer only hearing the name) whom Lord Egremont had originally engaged to tutor his son but later put through Oxford and installed as rector of Petworth. He was involved in the education of the young F.H. Arnold, and he may well have been instrumental in inspiring his botanical interest. Had the Monkey Orchid been found growing naturally in or around Petworth, Arnold would definitely have included it in his Flora of Sussex and probably mentioned it elsewhere in his writings. We can only conclude – assuming that Sokot=Sockett – that the specimen was obtained outside the county. It is now only known for certain in Kent and Oxfordshire.'

LAX-FLOWERED ORCHID

Orchis laxiflora Lamarck

In 1987 as part of the Kew Sainsbury Orchid Project, 350 seedlings of Lax-flowered Orchid were planted out at The Slips in Wakehurst Place, where they continue to flourish. The seed came from a plant pollinated at Kew in 1983, and originally collected in Crete. The experiment was designed to demonstrate that laboratory-raised seedlings could be successfully transferred to the wild. The species was chosen as one that does not exist in Great Britain and is easy to identify.

In 1993 seed was collected from the native Jersey population and propagated, but returned to Jersey – not planted out at Wakehurst.

TONGUE ORCHID

Serapias lingua L.

In 1998 a single flowering plant appeared unexpectedly with the Lax-flowered Orchids at Wakehurst Place, with four in 1999 and eleven in 2000. There is no evidence that it was planted, and it was not part of the ongoing project for *Orchis laxiflora*.
Seedlings of *Orchis morio* were planted out in 1987 and of *Dactylorhiza fuchsii* in 1989, and it is possible that the Tongue Orchids came in accidentally with seedlings of either planting. *Serapias lingua, S.parviflora* and *S.vomeracea* were all reared in the same glasshouse at Kew as the other orchids.

Some Notes on Hybrid Orchids in Sussex

Cephalanthera damasonium x *C. longifolia*
Leaves broad and ridged, flowers borne on long pedicels parallel to the stem. Flowers pure white, perianth segments long and spreading. Labellum with three ridges on the base. Ovaries intermediate in thickness with 180° anticlockwise twist. Found near Chichester by Brianne Reeve (1995) and near Arundel (D.C. Lang 1996 and 2000).

Right: ***Cephalanthera damasonium* x *C. longifolia*.**
Below: ***Gymnadenia conopsea* x *Dactylorhiza fuchsii***

Epipactis helleborine x *E. purpurata*
Found by J.T.H. Knight near Horsham (1959). Detailed description lacking.

Gymnadenia conopsea x *Dactylorhiza fuchsii*
Not uncommon on the downs. Leaves long and narrow but lightly spotted. Labellum shape like *Gymnadenia* but all segments marked with dots and loops. Spur long and decurved, flowers scented. Wolstonbury (1994), Ringmer (1966), Caburn (1987 and 1988), Beddingham (1991 and 2000) and Alciston (1979 and 1999).

Gymnadenia conopsea x *Dactylorhiza maculata* ssp. *ericetorum*
(Noted as *Orchis maculata*). In Wolley-Dod (1937) as found on the downs near Plumpton and Alciston. This is highly unlikely, and it was probably the hybrid *Gymnadenia conopsea* x *Dactylorhiza fuchsii*.

Platanthera bifolia x *Dactylorhiza fuchsii*
Recorded by E.J. Bedford but may not have been collected in Sussex. Plain labellum shaped like that of *Dactylorhiza fuchsii*, but with a long, decurved spur and spreading lateral perianth segments like a *Platanthera*.

Platanthera bifolia x *Dactylorhiza maculata* ssp. *ericetorum*
Recorded from Pressridge Warren on Ashdown Forest by Miss Saunders in June 1931. Not a certain record.

Ophrys apifera x *O. insectifera*
Recorded near Arundel (1998), only the second European record for a wild plant, and the first in Sussex. Growth form and outer perianth segments like *Ophrys insectifera.* Upper inner segments like *Ophrys apifera*, labellum convex with small furry humps on either side of the base, and a broad blue band across the middle. Flowered again in 1999 and 2000.

Dactylorhiza fuchsii x *D. incarnata*
Growth form like *D.incarnata*, with keeled basal leaves and clasping stem leaves, heavily marked with brown spots and bars. Flowers like *D.incarnata*, pale mauve with spots and loops on the labellum. Sides of the labellum strongly folded down. Ferring Rife (1996).

Dactylorhiza fuchsii x *D. praetermissa*
A tall robust plant with a hollow stem. Leaves spotted, sometimes heavily. Dense conical flower spike with long narrow bracts. Labellum marked with loops and dots typical of *D.fuchsii*, but spur fat and conical. A common hybrid, with records from Leythorne, Chichester (1985), Arundel (2000), East Chiltington (1983 now destroyed), Malling Down (1994), Piltdown (1981), Cowden (1982), Newhaven (1989), Friston Forest (1973), Marshall Road, Eastbourne (1980 now destroyed), and Rye Harbour (1982).

Dactylorhiza maculata ssp.*ericetorum* x *D. praetermissa*
Reported in Wolley-Dod (1937) from Aldsworth Pond, near Fishbourne Church, near Chichester Canal and on Henfield Common. No floral details available. Plants I have seen other than in Sussex have long, narrow erect leaves. Labellum shallowly three-lobed, marked all over with a pattern of lines and dots. Spur long and straight, moderately thick.

E.J. Bedford reported it from Allington Farm near Cooksbridge. I know the site well and it is not suitable for *D.maculata* ssp. *ericetorum*. In my opinion the likely hybrid was *D. fuchsii* x *D. praetermissa*.

Above: *Ophrys apifera* x *O. insectifera*.
Left: *Dactylorhiza fuchsii* x *D. praetermissa*.

Past, Present and Future

Where nature is concerned, there is one thing of which you can be certain: nothing remains static. The process is dynamic and ever-changing.

The face of the Sussex countryside has changed enormously within my lifetime, while the changes which have occurred since the days of botanical pioneers such as William Borrer and Sir Joseph Woods in the late eighteenth century are hard for us to comprehend. Some changes are obvious – roads, railways and the vast spread of urban development – while others are more subtle and yet have a direct impact on our orchids. Wetlands have been drained with the loss of marsh- and bog-loving orchids; old meadows which had been grazed for centuries have been ploughed up; and ancient woodlands have been felled and replanted to the detriment of species such as the butterfly-orchids.

Even the Sussex Downs are much altered. You have only to read Gilbert White's account of riding from Selbourne to Ringmer in 1772 to appreciate the scale of the changes. Aerial photographs show how, in recent years, a great deal of our open downland has been lost to encroachment by scrub, despite the assertions I have heard from old folk that 'It's always been like that!' Many of the downland orchids, such as the Bee, Fragrant and Frog Orchids, are shadows of their former selves.

Heathlands remain as tiny fragments of their previous extent – drained, afforested and built upon – although Sussex has not suffered as badly as some other counties, such as Dorset. The forests of Worth, Tilgate and St Leonard's, with their unique mosaic of grazed fields and small woods, have totally vanished, and with them the Small-white Orchid. We still have the Ashdown Forest, albeit without its Bog Orchids.

All is not doom and gloom, however. Throughout the county, nature reserves have been set up to preserve the good things that remain, and to create an environment where, among many other things, plants such as orchids can re-establish and even increase. This is costly both in terms of money and physical effort, but thanks to the work of organisations such as English Nature, the Sussex Wildlife Trust, the Sussex Downs Conservation Board, the Environment Agency and the National Trust (together with the support that they receive from a veritable army of volunteers), there is good evidence that things are improving. The summer of 2000 was outstanding for downland orchids, the weather combining with the conservation effort of the past few years to produce the best flowering for a decade.

I have listed the organisations particularly involved with plant conservation, with their addresses and telephone numbers, at the end of this chapter. Supporting their work will ensure that we continue to have orchids to enjoy in Sussex, and they in turn are keen to encourge naturalists to visit and enjoy those reserves which are open to the public. Pamphlets are available for most reserves, with information about access, what to see and when to visit. Guided walks are arranged to certain reserves in the summer time, and this is an excellent way for the beginner to learn in congenial company.

We are constantly hearing of the dire consequences of global warming, but it may not turn out to be a total disaster. We may see the loss of cold-loving alpine plants from the north of Great Britain, but with the possible slow warming of our climate we may also reasonably hope to see those orchids which have shown some evidence of spreading northwards through France, Germany and Holland making the jump across the Channel. Where better to expect them than in Sussex?

The Short-spurred Fragrant Orchid (*Gymadenia odoratissima*) was recorded many years ago on oolitic limestone in Durham, but it has recently been recorded further north in France than previously and is a good candidate to join the Sussex list. Two varieties of Bee Orchid have been recorded recently close to Sussex – var.*friburgensis* in Wiltshire and var.*belgarum* in Hampshire. We should look out for their presence in West Sussex on the chalk.

A few possible newcomers to look out for in Sussex. Clockwise, from top left: *Ophrys apifera* var. *belgarum*, *Serapius cordigera*, *Serapias parviflora*, and *Ophrys apifera* var. *friburgensis*.

The Tongue-orchids have also shown evidence of moving up through France to the Normandy and Brittany coasts. *Serapias parviflora* occurred in East Cornwall from 1989-1998, *Serapias cordigera* turned up in east Kent in 1996 and flowered again in 1997, while *Serapias lingua* occurred in Guernsey in 1992 and in South Devon in 1998. The last record involved a possible Algerian sub-species (ssp.*duriuei*), with the possibility that viable seed or micro-tubers were windblown along with Saharan sand, which falls every now and then in Sussex as 'red rain'. There is even an old record for *Serapias neglecta* from a cornfield on the Isle of Wight in 1918.

Those who seek shall find!

Recording

This bring me to the subject of how we can make a useful, long-lasting physical record of the orchids that we find.

I must admit to a sinking feeling when viewing herbarium sheets covered with rare pressed flowers, yet they are indisputably of enormous historical value – gathered at a time when there were no specialist floras to help in identification and no cameras to record them, let alone in colour.

One method that I do recommend for preserving material involves removing just one single flower from the spike, dissecting the floral parts and mounting them on a card under sellotape. (See illustration below.) There is minimal damage to the plant if it is done with care, and such reference cards are easily stored with all the data written on them, and can be sent by post to experts to examine. Material must be fresh when mounted. Colour fades rapidly, but markings remain clear for many years.

1. The flower is removed with its bract intact. Store in an airtight tube if not processing immediately, or it will shrivel.

2. A wide (2-3cm) piece of sellotape is fixed on a surface, sticky side up.

3. Floral parts are cut off with a scalpel blade and, using forceps, are placed face down on the sellotape. The sequence I use is bract; three outer perianth segments; upper inner perianth segments with labellum; and finally the spur, cut through as close to its origin as possible.

4. The sellotape strip is lifted and, with great care, placed on the card sticky side down. The assemblage is then smoothed out. Trim off surplus sellotape.

5. All necessary data is written on the card.

This procedure should not be used for any rare or endangered species. When in doubt do not collect material, but take photographs only.

I cannot stress sufficiently strongly the value of accurate recording of plants, both for personal interest and as an archival source of information for future generations. Data should include the number of flowering plants, dates of flowering, variations or abnormalities, evidence of insect pollinators and, most importantly, an accurate desciption of the site with an equally accurate map reference. The use of hand-held GPS (global positioning satellite) recorders gives such an accurate fix that sites can be determined to within 10m, an invaluable aid in dense woodlands. Details of where to send orchid records are given on page 138.

Protection of plants in the wild

In 1999 the Botanical Society of the British Isles (BSBI) published a 'Code of Conduct for the conservation and enjoyment of wild plants, copies of which may be obtained from BSBI at The Natural History Museum, Cromwell Road, London SW7 5BD.

This is a most useful booklet, which I thoroughly recommend. It clearly sets out the law relating to wild plants and the steps we should take to ensure that we do not damage the very things we set out to enjoy. The following are some important points covered in the Code:

1. Under the Wildlife and Countryside Act (1981) it is illegal to uproot any wild plant without the permission of the landowner or occupier.

2. Under the Act, Schedule 8 lists endangered plants which may not be picked, uprooted or destroyed except under licence. The Sussex orchids included in the schedule are: Red Helleborine, Lizard Orchid, Late Spider-orchid, Early Spider-orchid and Military Orchid.

3. Plants in protected areas such as National Nature Reserves (NNRs), Sites of Special Scientific Interest (SSSIs) and similar areas may not be destroyed without prior consultation with the statutory conservation agencies.

4. Plants listed in the National Red Data Book and the County Rare Plants Register may not be picked for pleasure.

5. Collecting small amounts of plant material for identification (not always possible in the field), herbaria etc., is acceptable except in the case of protected or Red List species. Do not collect if you are in doubt or if the population is small.

6. Photography should be done with discretion and without unnecessary 'gardening' around the subject, which may make it obvious to the ill-intentioned. When photographing, take care not to damage neighbouring plants.

Conservation organisations in Sussex

The Sussex Wildlife Trust, Woods Mill, Henfield, West Sussex BN5 9SD (Tel 01273 492630; fax 01273 494500)

Sussex Downs Conservation Board, Chanctonbury House, Church Street, Storrington, West Sussex RH20 4LT (Tel 01903 741234; fax 01903 741241)

The Environment Agency (Sussex Area Office), Saxon House, Little High Street, Worthing, West Sussex BN11 1DH (Tel 0645 333111)

English Nature, Phoenix House, 32-33 North Street, Lewes, East Sussex BN72PH (Tel 01273 476595; fax 01273 483063)

The National Trust (Southern, including West Sussex), Polesden Lacey, Dorking, Surrey RH5 6BD (tel 01372 453401; fax 01372 452023)

The National Trust (Kent & East Sussex), Scotney Castle, Lamberhurst, Kent TN3 8JN (Tel 01892 890651; fax 01892 890110)

Plant Life, 21 Elizabeth Street, London SW1W 9RP (Tel 020 780 0100; fax 020 7730 8377)

Herbaria

The following list includes all the museums that I have visited during research for this book, and in each case lists in alphabetical order the names of those botanists who have made a herbarium collection lodged at that museum. I hope that this will prove useful to anyone else whose study is exclusively of orchids in Sussex.

Bexhill Museum
M.Cobbe H.L.Green J.W.G. P.Stockdale

Booth Museum of Natural History, Brighton
F.H.Arnold Baines S.Derrick P.Harland T.Hilton F.C.S.Roper U.Smith D.E.de Vesian

British Museum of Natural History
R.S.Adamson F.H.Arnold W.C.Barton E.J.Bedford A.Bennett J.T.I.Boswell-Syme J.E.Cooper E.S.Gregory N & J.Groves P.M.Hall F.J.Hanbury T.Hilton D.H.Kent F.C.King C.C.Lacaita J.Linnell E.F.Linton H.C.Littlebury A.H.Maude R.Meinertzhagen W.W.Newbould F.W.Payne H.W.Pugsley J.Roffey F.C.S.Roper C.E.Salmon E.S.Salmon P.Sewell J.Sowerby R.S.Standen E.Vaughan A.H.Wolley-Dod C.A.Wright D.P.Young

Eastbourne Museum
No orchid material

Hastings Museum
No orchid material

Kew Orchid Herbarium
E.J.Bedford W.Biddicombe M.S.Blaker W.Borrer C.E.Britton O.Buckle B.F.Bunyard Cotter M.Cubitt M.Deans G.C.Druce R.Edwards M.Elms A.A.Evans Fielder A.G.Gregor H.L.F.Guermonprez A.R.Harwood C.Hawkins H.M.Hilton Hodgson E.Hope A.B.Jackson J.H.A.Jenner G.C.Joad J.Lightfoot Livesey B.T.Lowne M.Markwick E.Milne-Redhead E.Morris G.W.R.Morris W.E.Nicholson D.Philcox W.W.A.Phillips K.Pickard H.J.Riddlesdell C.E.Salmon A.Saunders F.Senoglos Sharpe V.S.Summerhayes C.B.Tahourdin D.Turner M.Turrill V.H.Vick S.R.Vine H.C.Watson E.Y.Western C.H.Wright

Maidstone Museum
F. Rose

National Museum of Wales, Cardiff
N.Ballard R.Boniface G.L.B L.Downing G.C.Druce T.A.Dymes E.B.Harris C.Hedge W.S.Lacey J.E.Lousley E.S.Marshall J.M.Milner B.M.Oakshott M.Richards F.Rose W.A.Shoolbred P.J.Wanstall

Portsmouth City Council Museum
F.F.Davies H.Foster H.L.F.Guermonprez Reynolds

Reading University Herbarium
W.M.Abbott-Anderson E.N.Bloomfield J.A.Broadbent J.B.Duncan A.Fielder J.E.Lousley C.B.Tahourdin H.Taylor E.C.Wallace

Tunbridge Wells Civic Museum
M.W.Bostock L.M.Child R.A.Crowson A.Holden G.E.Shaw J.Stirling A.H.Wolley-Dod

English Nature Offices, Lewes
Scientific files on all SSSIs in West and East Sussex.

Sussex Biodiversity Centre, Woods Mill, Henfield (Sussex Wildlife Trust)
All orchid records for the county are held on computer.

Bibliography

Allen, D.E. (1983) The Herbaria of Joseph Woods *Watsonia* **14**:273-274

Arnold, F.H. (1875) Frog Orchis (*Coeloglossum viride*) Goodwood and Harting. *Sci-Gossip* **XI**:23
1887) *Cephalanthera ensifolia. Sci-Gossip* **XXIII**:140
(1887) 'Flora of Sussex' (Hamilton, Adams & Co.Chichester)

Bedford, E.J. (1912) Some Rare Sussex Orchids *Knowledge* **XXXV** - paper rep. *S.E.Nat*(**XX**) as (**XIX**) (1915) 1, **XXXIX**:72; **LII** (1947):16
(1923) Notes on two orchids new to East Sussex. *Proc.*L.S. (1913) 3; *Eastbourne N.H.S. N.S.II* (1912):50
(1914) *Orchis hircina . Journ.Bot.***LII**:311
(1920) *Orchis hircina* in Sussex. *Journ.Bot.*LVIII:201

Borrer, W. (1860) *Ophrys aranifera* (=*sphegodes*) Pulborough. *Phyt.N.S.***IV**:256

Bray, E. (1900) *Habenaria (Coeloglossum) viride* Beachy Head. Frog-orchis in Sussex. *Sci-Gossip N.S.***VII**:54

Briggs, M. (1990) Obituary, Oliver Buckle (1903-1989) *Watsonia* **18**:11

Brooke. B.J. (1948) 'The Military Orchid' 51, 52, 76

Brooke, B.J. and Rose, F (1940) A New British Species of *Epipactis. Journ Bot.* **76**:337-41

C.T.P. (1971) Obituary, Donald Peter Young. *Proc.Croydon Nat.Hist.Soc.* **XIV**(9):225-227

Carey, P.D. (1999) Changes in the distribution and abundance of *Himantoglossum hircinum* (L.)Sprengel (Orchidaceae) over the last 100 years. *Watsonia* **22**:353-364

Crane, M.D. (....) Henry Leopold Foster Guermonprez (1858-1924) Portsmouth City Museum

Deakin, R. (1871) 'The Flowering Plants of Tunbridge Wells and Neighbourhood. (Stidolph, Bellamy and Groombridge)

Desmond, R. (...) Dictionary of British and Irish Botanists and Horticulturalists.'

Dony, J.G. (1977) J.Edward Lousley (1907-1976) *Watsonia* **II**:282-286

Ettlinger,D.M.T. (1991) Two new varieties of British Dactylorhiza *Dactylorhiza fuchsii* var.*rhodochila* D.M.T.Ettlinger var.*nova*. *Watsonia* **18**:307-309
(1998) A new variety of *Ophrys apifera* Hudson (Orchidaceae) *Watsonia* **22**:105-107

Hall and Woodhouse, A. (1872-73) Orchidaceae with special reference to the species found Near Eastbourne *Eastbourne N.H.S.Sussex Orchids*

Hall, P.C. (1980) 'Sussex Plant Atlas' (Booth Museum of Natural History, Brighton)

Hemsley, W.B. (1868) Notes on the flora of Sussex *Journ.Bot.***VI**:194, 258

Hilton, T. (1900) *Ophrys apifera* Beachy Head. Pale-coloured Bee-orchis *Sci-Gossip N.S.***VII**:54

Hoare, A.G. (1980) '*Anacamptis pyramidalis* (L.)Rich. in Sussex'. *B.S.B.I. News* **24**:27

Horsfield, T.W. (1835) History, antiquities and topography of the county of Sussex Vol.II Appendix 2 (T.H.Cooper)

Hutchings, M.J. (1987) 'The population biology of the Early Spider Orchid *Ophrys sphegodes* Mill. 1. A demographic study from 1975-1984'. *J.Ecol.***75**:711-27
(1987) 'The population biology of the Early Spider Orchid *Ophrys sphegodes* Mill. 2. Temporal patterns in behaviour'. *J.Ecol.* **75**:729-42

Jenkinson, M. (1991) 'Wild Orchids of Dorset' (Orchid Sundries Ltd.)
(1995) 'Wild Orchids of Hampshire and the Isle of Wight'. (Orchid Sundries Ltd.)
Jenner, J.H.A. (1911) Sussex Orchids - *Orchis purpurea* near Lewes and *Orchis hircinum* near Eastbourne. *Journ.Bot.* **XLIX**:276
Knight, J.T.H. (1959) Notes on a colony of Epipactis in the Sussex Weald (Horsham) *B.S.B.I. News* **3**:279
Lang, D.C. and Lansley,J.L.S. (1978) *Cephalanthera damasonium* (Mill.) Druce x *C.longifolia* (L.) Fritsch. *Watsonia*12:49-50
Lang, D. (1980) 'Orchids of Britain' (Oxford University Press) (1989) 'A Guide to the Wild Orchids of Great Britain and Ireland' (Oxford University Press)
Minnis, J. (1989) ' E.J.Bedford of Lewes. Photographs of the London, Brighton and South Coast Railway' (Wild Swan Publications Ltd.)
Nazarov, V.V. and Efetov,K.A. (1993) On the role of Zygaenidae (Lepidoptera) in pollination of *Anacamptis pyramidalis* (Orchidaceae) *Zool.Zhurn.***72**:54-67
Nilsson, L.A. (1983) Mimesis of bellflower (campanula) by the red helleborine orchid *Cephalanthera rubra. Nature* **305**:799-800
Rich, T.G.C. (1995) Phyllis Stockdale (C.1898-1949)
Rich, T. et al (1996) 'Flora of Ashdown Forest' (Sussex Botanical Recording Society)
Robinson, M. (1945) Joys and Sorrows of a South Downs Botanist. *The Sussex County Magazine* **XIX**(8):186-189
Roper, F.C.S. (1881) Notes on the flora of East Sussex *Journ.Bot.* **XIX**:369-373
(1882) Notes on the flora of East Sussex *Journ.Bot.***XX** (Note XI of new series):360-362
Rose, F. (1976) Three forms of *Gymnadenia conopsea* (pers.comm.)
(1988) Obituary. Edward Charles Wallace (1909-1986) *Watsonia* **17**:116-117
(1988) *Gymnadenia conopsea* (L.) R.Br., in Rich,T.G.C. et al *Plant Crib*:380
(1991) A new subspecies of *Gymnadenia conopsea* (L.) R.Br. *Watsonia* **18**:319-320
(1995) 'The Habitats and Vegetation of Sussex'. (Booth Museum of Natural History, Brighton)
Rose, F. and Davey, S.R. (1996) The three forms of Fragrant Orchid *B.S.B.I.News* **72**:71
Sharp, J. (1845) On the rediscovery of Ray's habitat for *Malaxis paludosa* at Tunbridge Wells Phyt.**11**:42 (E.Jenner l.c.79)
Smail, H.C.P. (1974) William Borrer of Henfield, botanist and horticulturalist. 1781-1862 *Watsonia* **10**:55-60
Smith, U. and Howard, E. (1997) 'A History of Sussex Wild Plants'. (Booth Museum of Natural History, Brighton)
Stearn, W.T. (1979) William Turner (c.1508-1568) and Job Edward Lousley (1907-1976) a Commemorative address. *Biol.Journ.Linn.Soc.***14**:467-471
Steel, D. and Creed, P. (1982) 'Wild Orchids of Berkshire, Buckinghamshire and Oxfordshire (Pisces Publications,Oxford)
Tahourdin, C.B. (1925) Some notes to British Orchids: 1-7
(1926-27) Some notes on British Orchids: 1-11
Tyler, J. (1999) British *Orchidaceae* - their pollinators (pers.comm.)
Willis, A.J. (1980) '*Ophrys apifera* Huds x *O.insectifera* L. a natural hybrid in Britain'. *Watsonia* **13**:97-102
Wilmott, A.J. (1933) *Orchis hircinum* (Glynde) *Journ.Bot.***LXXI**:107
Wolley-Dod, A.H. (1937) 'Flora of Sussex' (Ed.) (Kenneth Saville, Hastings)
Young, D.P. (1962) Studies in the British *Epipactis* v. *Epipactis leptochila. Watsonia* **5**:127-142

Glossary

Aberrant: a form which deviates from the normal type
Acid: water or soils containing free acids with a pH value less than 7. Such soils lack chalk or lime
Acuminate: gradually tapering to a point
Albinism: characteristic shown by plants which are albino
Albino: a plant which shows a congenital lack of the usual colour pigments, normally the reds and blues,. Green pigments are still present
Alien: not native. Introduced to a region deliberately or accidentally by man
Alkaline: pertaining to water or soils containing lime, potash etc., with a pH value greater than 7
Autogamous: applied to a flower which is self-pollinating

Base rich: pertaining to a soil containing large amounts of basic substances, such as compounds of calcium, potassium or magnesium
Bog: a wet marshy area overlying acid peat
Bract: a small leaf-like structure at the base of a flower stalk
Bulbil: a small bulb arising on the leaf edge, or between the leaf and stem of a plant
Bursicle: a small flap or pouch which covers the viscidia and prevents them from drying out

Calcareous: pertaining to water or soils containing chalk or lime
Calcicole: showing a preference for calcareous habitat
Capsule: the seed-containing structure, composed of a number of carpels joined together, at the base of the flower
Carpel: one of the divisions of the capsule
Caudicle: the stalk by which the pollinium is attached to the viscidium at its base
Chlorophyll: the green pigment in most plant cells, which takes part in photosynthesis, the process of converting carbon dioxide and water into carbohydrates with energy from sunlight
Chromosome: one of the basic components of the cell nucleus, which carry the inherited characters of the organism
Ciliolate: bearing hairs
Cleistogamous: self-pollinating within a flower which does not fully open
Colony: a group of plants of the same type growing in a close and well-defined area
Column: a specialised structure in the centre of the orchid flower, the upper part of the female reproductive organ (stigma) and the lower part of the male reproductive organ (stamen)
Conjoined: joined together
Connivent: pertaining to structures which are separated at their bases, but touching at their apices
Cotyledon: the first leaves of a plant produced by the germinating seed
Crenate: with a scalloped edge

Dactylorchids: orchids belonging to the genus *Dactylorhiza*, having palmately divided tubers
DNA: desoxyribose nucleic acid
Dominant: pertaining to the most abundant plant form in a community, covering a significant fraction of the area

Ecology: the scientific study of the relationship between living organisms and their environment

Epichile: the outer part of the labellum of orchids of the genus Epipactis
Escarpment: a steep slope below a high land feature, such as a cliff
Etiolated: applied to a plant made pale and spindly by growing without adequate sunlight

F1: the first-generation offspring of a hybrid
F2: the second-generation resulting from crossing two F1 individuals
Factoid: a humorous term for a rumour or myth made acceptable by repetition
Family: a group of related genera
Fasciated: compressed together in a bundle
Fen: a wet area where peat is overlaid by alkaline water
Fertilisation: the process of uniting male and female reproductive cells
Flora: the plants of a particular region or environment
Flush: a wet area on a slope, formed where water flows out from a spring

Genetical: concerning the inheritable make-up of an organism
Genus: a group of related species
Ghyll: in the Sussex Weald, a steep-sided stream valley
Glabrous: hairless
Glaucous: bluish and usually smooth

Herbarium: a collection of dried plants, usually pressed (plural=herbaria)
Hood: the helmet shape formed by the connivent upper petals and sepals in certain orchid flowers
Hybrid: a plant originating from the fertilisation of one species by another
Hybridisation: the process by which a hybrid is formed
Hybrid swarm: a group of hybrids which show a range of characteristics between those of the two parent plants
Hypochile: the basal part of the labellum of orchids of the genus *Epipactis*

Intergeneric: applied to hybrids formed between species of two different genera
Intergradation: the process by which lack of distinctiveness between species permits hybridisation
Interspecific: applied to hybrids between plants of two different species
Introgression: the process of repeated back-crossing of an F1 hybrid with one of its parents

Keeled: describing leaves which are folded along a marked midrib, producing a shape like the keel of a boat

Labellum: the lip of the flower, in orchids the lower of the three petals, often large and complex in structure
Lanceolate: shaped like a lance head, tapering and pointed
Lax: loose, not closely packed

Marsh: a wet area overlying a soil not composed of peat
Monocarpic: pertaining to plants which flower once only and then die
Mycorrhiza: the fungus which invades the underground parts of many orchid species
Mycorrhizome: the underground structure first formed when an orchid seed germinates, usually infected with mycorrhizal fungus

Oolitic: pertaining to limestone composed of minute rounded concretions resembling fish roe
Ovary: the lower part of the female reproductive organ which contains the seeds

Palmate: divided like the fingers of a hand
Pedicel: the stalk of a single flower
Peloric: describing a flower with a radially symmetric arrangement of perianth members, while the species normally has an asymmetrical arrangement
Perennial: a plant living for more than two years
Perianth: the outer, non-reproductive parts of the flower, divided into an outer series (sepals) and an inner series (petals)
Petal: one of the segments of the inner whorl of the perianth
pH: negative logarithm of hydrogen-ion concentration in moles per litre, giving a measure of the alkalinity or acidity of a solution or soil, pH7 being neutral, values above 7 being alkaline and less than 7 acid
Pheromones: chemicals which act as sexual attractants
Photosynthesis: the process of converting carbon dioxide and water into carbohydrates using energy from sunlight
Phylogeny: racial evolution of a plant type
Pollination: transference of pollen from the male reproductive organ (stamen) to the female reproductive organ (stigma)
Pollinia: structures formed by the coherence of pollen grains into a mass (single - pollinium)
Proboscis: elongated flexible mouthparts of an insect
Protocorm: microscopic first-development stage of growth of an orchid from seed
Pseudobulb: a bulb-like swelling of the aerial stem, not a true bulb
Pseudocopulation: the attempt by a male insect to mate with a flower to which it has been attracted, a process by which the pollinia are removed and transferred to another flower

Quadrat: a sampling area of one metre square (or some other size) – the wooden frame used to outline the area

Raceme: an unbranched flower spike where the flowers are borne on pedicels
Rachis: the axis of a leaf, from its origin on the stem to its apex
Reflexed: folded back
Relict: the last members of a population which has mostly disappeared
Rhizome: an underground stem, usually growing horizontally, and lasting for more than one season
Rhizomatous: like a rhizome
Rosette: a group of leaves arranged around the base of a stem like the petals of a rose, often flat on the ground
Rostellum: the sterile third stigma of an orchid flower, situated between the stamens and the two functional stigmas. Often long and beak-shaped, bearing the viscidia of the pollinia

Saprophytic: a plant which obtains its nutrition from the breakdown of dead plant or animal material
Semi-peloric: describing as flower in which the abnormal perianth members give a misleading appearance of being peloric. In the semi-peloric Bee Orchid the labellum resembles the sepals. If it were truly peloric it would resemble the antenna-like upper petals
Sepal: one of the segments of the outer whorl of the perianth
Sessile: without a stalk
Species: a group of individuals having common characteristics, a division of a genus
Spike: an elongated unbranched flower head
Spur: an elongated pouch formed at the base of the labellum
Stamen: one of the male reproductive organs
Stigma: the receptive upper part of the female reproductive organ
Stolon: an above-ground creeping stem

Sub-glabrous: almost hairless
Sub-species: a division of a species, distinguished only by very slight variation, insufficient to accord it the rank of a separate species
Swarm: a group of hybrids showing a range of characteristics between those of the parent plants
Symbiosis: two organisms existing together to their mutual benefit

Taxa: divisions of plant classification such as genera or species (single - taxon)
Taxonomy: the principles and study of classification
Terracettes: narrow flat platforms formed on a slope, often by the passing feet of grazing animals
Tetrad: here applied to a square with an area of 4 square kilometres, bounded by sides of 2 kilometres
Tribe: a group of plants of a rank between a genus and a sub-family
Tuber: a swollen part of a stem or root not persisting for more than a year, tubers of successive years not arising from one another. Food stores

Valve: one of the segments of a capsule which splits to allow seeds to disperse
Variation: difference in characteristics within a species
Variety: a division of a species showing some minor differences in character
Vasculum: a metal case for transporting plant specimens in the field
Vector: an agent, insect or otherwise, involved in carrying pollen from one flower to another
Vegetative: concerned with growth and development
Vegetative multiplication: the increase in the number of individuals by an asexual process
Vice-county: the sub-division of a county into a smaller unit more suitable for recording species distribution
Viscidia: the sticky discs at the base of the pollinia which glue the pollen masses on to a visiting insect (single - viscidium)

Where to send orchid records

Each county has a Recorder, appointed by the Botanical Society of the British Isles (BSBI), an amateur organisation covering the whole of the British Isles. The Recorder for West or East Sussex can be contacted at the BSBI, c/o The Natural History Museum, Cromwell Road, London SW7 5BD (Tel 0207 942 5002).

The Sussex Botanical Recording Society is an amateur group dedicated to the study and recording of plants in Sussex. There are more than a hundred members active throughout the county. Records can be sent to: The Secretary, The Sussex Botanical Recording Society, c/o The Sussex Wildlife Trust, Woods Mill, Henfield, West Sussex BN5 9SD (Tel 01273 492630; fax 01273 494500)

The Sussex Wildlife Trust holds the data for the Sussex Biodiversity Record Centre, acting as the clearing house for information. They will pass it to the appropriate BSBI county Recorder and to the Sussex Botanical Recording Society.

Confidentiality for any rare species will always be respected, and help and advice can be obtained concerning the identification of difficult species.

Index